Better Outcomes

Better Outcomes

A Guide to Humanizing Healthcare

Rafael E. Salazar II, MHS, OTR/L

BEP

BUSINESS EXPERT PRESS

Leader in applied, concise business books

Description

We have a problem in healthcare.

That problem is this: in today's healthcare environment, especially in the United States, people take a back seat to the numbers in almost every aspect of healthcare service delivery. Productivity, utilization, and other business metrics rule the roost.

If it's not calculatable, spreadsheet-able, or measurable, it hardly receives any attention from healthcare managers, administrators, and decision-makers.

We can't simply sit back and allow the dehumanization that currently runs rampant in our clinics and hospitals continue to wreak havoc on one of the most important factors in clinical outcomes: the relationships between healthcare professionals and the people (patients) that they serve.

Healthcare is a great and noble profession, but it will only remain so if we, as healthcare professionals, return its focus to its true purpose: people, the people receiving care, and the people working to deliver that care. After all, we're all more than simply numbers on spreadsheets or items on checklists.

Better Outcomes: A Guide for Humanizing Healthcare outlines the 8 changes that organizations and clinicians need to commit to in order to return to the focus of healthcare to where it should be: *the patient.*

The book covers topics related to truly *patient-centered care*, a *biopsychosocial approach* to service delivery, *patient engagement, interpersonal communication*, and developing *long-term relationships* with patients.

Through an exploration of both clinical research and real-life examples and cases, the book outlines and supports a vision of a new healthcare, where skilled, competence, and caring clinicians care for engaged patients to promote better clinical outcomes, deliver unmatched satisfaction, and lasting relationships.

Keywords

healthcare; patient care; healthcare management; healthcare administration; patient centered care; biopsychosocial model; healthcare communication; relationship-based care; value-based healthcare; value-based reimbursement; patient engagement; patient experience; clinical leadership; healthcare reform

Contents

Acknowledgments

I always hate trying to enumerate and list the countless people who have supported me over the years and helped make this book a reality. I will undoubtedly leave someone off this list, and for that, I apologize.

To start, I would like to acknowledge and thank my wife, Natalie. I once heard someone say that the key to success is to marry well. I, for one, have found this to be true. Natalie's love and support over the years has truly made possible the career, impact, and accomplishments I can claim. From the initial decision to leave the secure employment of the VA, she has encouraged me, trusted in me, and motivated me to reach my full potential. For that, I am forever grateful. I'd also like to acknowledge my children, Rafa, Joseph, Nathan, Bridget, and Leah. They bring my life so much joy and meaning (as well as the drive to do well, so I can feed them as they grow up!).

Countless colleagues and business associates have helped me clarify my thinking and offered support and encouragement over the course of my career to date.

I want to thank Paul Sterett (https://whitehartinsight.com), for supporting and encouraging me in the early stages of my entrepreneurial journey. From helping me create a website, to discussing business over a drink, I have valued our friendship and am grateful for the encouragement, inspiration, and motivation he has provided over the years.

Another group of folks that deserve mentioning is the wonderful group of professionals I have had the amazing opportunity to work with since I began consulting in the field of disabilities and community integration. First of them is Derrick Dufresne (CRA Consulting). He provided me with the opportunity to step into my entrepreneurial journey by taking a chance and contracting with me to work on the Georgia project. I am forever grateful for the guidance, mentorship, advice, and wisdom he has imparted to me over the years. Bryon Dockter, Laura Paradowski, and Noelle Humphrey took me under their wing as a fledgling consultant, showed me the ropes, and provided guidance and comradery on that first project and on into other ventures. I have been truly blessed to call them not only colleagues, but friends. Lastly, Dan Howell has provided guidance, a listening ear, and advice on our work both on the Georgia project and in new business ventures. All five of these professionals have big hearts, great vision, and I am proud to have been able to work with them over the years to advance care, inclusion, and accessibility for adults with intellectual and developmental disabilities.

I would also like to acknowledge the faculty and staff at the Augusta University Department of Occupational Therapy during my tenure as an assistant professor in the department. They did so much to support me as I began my academic and teaching career. As a newly minted academic and faculty member, they took the time to provide guidance, mentorship, and assistance during my time teaching in the department. This again is another group of professionals with big hearts, great vision, and an unwavering commitment to bettering healthcare practice and service delivery.

I would also like to mention the members on the Board of Directors for the National Board for Certification in Occupational Therapy (NBCOT), as well as the staff at NBCOT I have had the pleasure to work with. As a younger, up-and-coming Occupational Therapy (OT) leader, I have been grateful for the warm welcome, support, and advice I have received during my time on the Board. As an Occupational Therapist, it has truly been a highlight of my OT career to serve alongside them.

One final group that deserves mentioning (like I said, there's a lot of people I have to thank!) is the wonderful team at my private practice, ProActive Rehabilitation and Wellness. The commitment to our patients, the friendly environment, and comradery each of them brings to the team makes going to work each day a blessing and a joy. Working with them over the past couple of years has fueled my passion for patient care, and provided me new insights into the world of healthcare; many of which influenced parts of this book.

Again, this section often ends up being the most difficult to write, because I know I have left some people off this list. If I failed to mention you, please forgive me. As much as our culture might try to convince us, no one is truly "self-made." We all rely on our social network, support system, and the work of those who have gone before us. I wouldn't be where I am today without the countless people who helped me, answered my questions, provided opportunities, and even given me critical feedback along the way.

Introduction

Let's Get Real

Let's get real: Healthcare is broken. You know it. I know it. Every clinician who came into this field from a desire to care for others knows this to be undeniably true. We feel it every day when we enter our clinics, hospitals, and practices. We feel the burden of time-based productivity metrics, utilization rates, and the expectation to behave like cogs in a giant, soul-crushing machine aimed at extracting revenue from our patients in exchange for "units" of treatment.

Day after day, millions of patients go to clinics, hospitals, and other healthcare facilities to address issues related to their physical, emotional, and mental health. More often than not, they experience indifference from providers and staff members; or find themselves bulldozed by procedures. And that's not surprising when the healthcare environment pushes clinicians to the point of burnout and apathy.

Healthcare should be about one thing: PEOPLE! Yet, how many clinics, organizations, or healthcare professionals live their lives by the numbers? Metrics and spreadsheets drive most of our healthcare decision makers and administrators. That leaves patients—the people we serve—lost in the mix. Patient's feel lost, forgotten, and ignored by a system that prioritizes efficiency and productivity over their own personal experiences, priorities, or goals.

That's probably why nearly 70 percent of patients never complete their course of care [1].

It's time for clinicians to finally stand up and say what we've all been thinking for so long: enough is enough!

It's time for healthcare organizations to commit to serving the individual needs of each unique patient that they are charged with serving.

To do this, we need a new framework, a new paradigm, a new way of looking at this noble profession of healthcare.

Below are the eight foundational commitments, as I see them, to create a new healthcare:

- Commitment #1: Adopt a Biopsychosocial Approach
- Commitment #2: Build Meaningful Relationships
- Commitment #3: Put People Ahead of Policies
- Commitment #4: Confidently Communicate Value
- Commitment #5: Prioritize Patient Engagement
- Commitment #6: Embrace Transparency
- Commitment #7: Forget Time-based Productivity
- Commitment #8: Lead Our Patients

What's This Book About?

As you may probably guess, this book is about what I'm calling "A Guide to Humanizing Healthcare." We have a problem in healthcare. That problem is this: in today's healthcare environment, especially in the United States, people take a back seat to the numbers in almost every aspect of healthcare service delivery. Productivity, utilization, and other business metrics rule the roost.

If it's not calculatable, spreadsheet-able, or measurable, it hardly receives any attention from healthcare managers, administrators, and decision makers.

This leads to situations we've all encountered when receiving some sort of healthcare service or treatment: situations that place processes and procedures over people.

I know you've experienced this: You arrive at a clinic of a new provider, fill out all of the new patient paperwork, and wait. Maybe, some of that paperwork doesn't apply to you. Maybe, you have a unique circumstance. Or maybe, for whatever reason, it would be simpler, easier, and more efficient to bypass some part of the "new patient onboarding" process at that clinic.

Is that an option?

Nope.

You go through the process, just like everyone else. You're just a number on a spreadsheet, working your way through the streamlined "process" that some consultant somewhere came up with to make that clinic "more efficient."

Often, these processes are meant to increase efficiency, reduce cost, and improve profitability. What they actually end up doing is impersonalizing the entire experience of seeking out healthcare services and treatment.

Now, there's nothing wrong with improving profitability. (We all want have families to feed, right?) The problem comes when the drive for profitability overrides the unique needs of the patients our clinics aim to serve.

I love this quote by John C. Bogle, founder of the Vanguard Group, when discussing our U.S. healthcare system:

> … the human concerns of the caregiver and the human needs of the patient have been overwhelmed by the financial interests of commerce (Bogle 2008, 125) [2].

How true is that today across healthcare in the United States?

It seems that healthcare organizations consistently place financial metrics, processes, and procedures ahead of the most important aspect of healthcare: the people providing and receiving that care.

How do we overcome that?

How do we radically improve clinical outcomes and patient experiences while at the same time rapidly increasing innovation, decreasing the cost of care, and improving our business metrics?

By committing to radically change the way, we operate our clinics and healthcare organizations.

Pat of this involves mastering what I call the Patient Relationship Cycle. Like I said earlier, healthcare is ultimately a human experience. Humans are, biologically, behaviorally, and psychologically social creatures. We have managed to climb to the top of the evolutionary ladder precisely because of our ability to cooperate and work together. We are wired to be social. We are wired to develop relationships.

The same rule applies to healthcare—or any service-based industry. At its core, healthcare revolves around human interactions and interpersonal communication. In order to maximize outcomes and impact, the human—or social—element must be accounted for. You must deal with the "touchy-feely" side of things. You must act human.

This book aims to provide a guide to help refocus healthcare back to that fundamental truth. It aims to provide a vision for how organizations and even individual clinicians can provide high-quality care, in a sustainable and profitable way, while putting the patient back in the center of the services they receive.

By adopting the eight commitments for a new healthcare, you will set your practice, clinic, or organization on a path to offering high-value, high-impact services and developing strong, lasting relationships with your patients.

What's in It for You, the Reader?

So, what do you get out of spending your valuable time with your nose in this book?

I mean, if you're like most clinicians or healthcare administrators, your daytime hours are consumed mostly by documentation, charges/billing, direct patient care, compliance issues, and the like.

As I mentioned earlier, this book will provide you with both a vision and a guide for providing high-quality care that focuses on the patient. It's what I call truly patient-centered care. It will provide concrete strategies and tactics for understanding, communicating, and implementing the necessary changes to return the focus of your practice to where it belongs: the patient.

While I provide references for relevant studies, research, and literature on the subjects we discuss in the book, I've only included a few simple illustrations when necessary to communicate the fundamentals of an idea. That way, you don't have to wade through mind-numbing statistics, charts, graphs, T-values, and all that other information that could cause you to lose sight of the fundamental core message of each chapter.

I've tried to include real-life, practical examples of each principle and its application so that you are able to better understand them. Hopefully, you will find these examples helpful in putting this information to use in your own clinical practice, clinic, or organization.

Read this book and you will walk away with an understanding of the current healthcare environment, its limitations and dysfunctions, and how you—as an individual clinician, clinic manager, executive, or owner—can begin to take real, meaningful steps to create better outcomes for both clinicians and patients who work for or receive care from your organization.

How to Get the Most Out of This Book?

The book's organization consists of the introduction (you're already halfway done with that!), a chapter for each of the eight commitments, and a summary chapter that lays out the vision for a new healthcare. Each of the chapters adds to the foundation for the final chapter; the chapter that describes what a new healthcare can look like.

Some of you, may skip all the way to the end … I get it: skip the fluff, get to the meat. However, each chapter provides the background, perspective, and lens through which all of the recommendations, insights, and conclusions are drawn from.

That being said, I highly encourage you to read—and understand—each chapter/commitment before moving on to the rest of the book. Odds are that these topics aren't be out-of-the-blue, groundbreaking, or even novel topics for clinicians and healthcare professionals. However, the insights, understandings, and implications drawn from each commitment form the basis of creating this new healthcare. Even if you've studied one of these topics in detail, it would be beneficial to read through them so that you can understand how I see them, and how they influence the views, insights, and recommendations in this book.

To get the most value out of this book, I suggest you don't try to read this in one sitting. We've all read books in our lives that are quick, easy reads that you can finish on a single flight or an afternoon. This is not one of those books. Again, this book is chalked full of resources, references, and based on "nerdy" literature. While I've distilled this information into clear, digestible bites, the fundamental principles of this book may require some additional thinking, reflecting, and more researching on your part to fully understand or implement them in your practice.

That leads me to the last two pieces of advice I have to get the most out of this book: (1) take notes and (2) keep this book handy. Since this book covers a wide breadth of material and makes unique suggestions and recommendations, you may find it helpful to take notes. You can do this in the margins on the book or on a separate document or paper. I've found that making my own notes on a book that I'm reading helps me understand, assimilate, and implement the information in a more effective way.

Also, since this book covers topics ranging from a novel view of healthcare to behavioral change, to interpersonal communication, it may be helpful to keep this book handy after you finish it. I imagine you'll find yourself reaching for it on an occasion when you run into various situations that require you to apply the principles of this book in a concrete way.

With that being said, thank you for taking the time to read this book. I truly hope it provides you with not only a new way of viewing healthcare, but also practical steps that you can take to begin delivering better outcomes to both your patients and the clinicians around you.

Rafael E. Salazar II, MHS, OTR/L
Principal Owner
Rehab U Practice Solutions
https://rehabupracticesolutions.com

CHAPTER 1

Commitment #1

Adopt a Biopsychosocial Approach

We will care for the whole person, not just a diagnosis. We will adopt a Biopsychosocial approach to healthcare, rejecting cookie-cutter treatment protocols with one-size-fits-most, plug-and-play protocols that fail to address the nuances of each individual patient.

As I have often written and said, there is always more at play than the issue or diagnosis that a patient is seeing you for. We are all people, and people are affected by biological, psychological, and environmental factors, each of which is unique to each individual. We cannot simply rely on a diagnosis or symptoms to determine which treatment option, assessment tool, or outcome measure will be most effective for each patient. Everything, including the patient's social environment, past experience, and readiness to change, impacts the issue they are now dealing with.

In the past, a biomedical model of practice placed symptoms, diagnoses, and physiological issues at the forefront of clinician's mind. While these factors are important, they represent only a fraction of the whole person, the individual patient, sitting in front of you now. It's time to start addressing individuals and their unique situations and factors, instead of focusing too heavily on diagnoses.

Since we understand how physical, psychological, and social/environmental factors interact throughout a patient's experience of a disease, injury, or illness, we understand that there are too many factors at play for rigid treatment protocols or "cookie-cutter" treatment programs.

Let's dive into that a bit more, by exploring what the Biopsychosocial (BSP for short) Model actually is.

What Is the BSP Model of Healthcare and How Does It Apply to Healthcare?

As I mentioned in Introduction, this book and the ideas contained within it are based on a few core principals. The first is this: Clinicians (and healthcare practitioners, in general) should adopt a BSP approach to service delivery.

Now, that's a big word, and a tangled concept. So, in this chapter, I attempt to provide a clear and succinct overview of the BSP Model of healthcare and how it can be applied to clinical practice, as well as its effects on patient experience and engagement in treatment.

In the past several years, the BSP Model has been all the rage on forums, social media, and in professional courses and trainings in the healthcare space. If you haven't been living under a rock for the last several years, you have likely heard the term biopsychosocial. Most likely, you've heard it referenced as the BSP Model of healthcare, or BSP treatment, or even heard it lumped in with "holistic care." But, what does that actually mean and how is it applied to clinical practice? That's what we're about to dive into.

Let's cover the basics:

- Define and describe the BSP Model of healthcare;
- Explore its application to clinical practice, specifically in the rehab world;
- Review relevant literature and research about the BSP Model;
- Explore how BSP factors can affect our patients' experience, perception, and even engagement and participation in the treatment we provide.

Defining the BSP Model

Let's begin with defining the BSP Model. For starters, the BSP Model has been described both as a philosophy of clinical care and a guide for clinical practice [1]. It proposes that suffering, disease, or illness involve a host of factors from biological (tissues, structures, and molecules) to environmental (social and psychological). Each of these factors affects a patient's subjective experience, clinical outcomes, and effect of treatment throughout the treatment process or course of a disease.

This approach to providing care considers the physical, psychological, and social factors of the disease or injury and promotes an integrated approach to treatment [2]. Like I mentioned earlier, it has become a rather popular and regularly studied topic over the past several years.

It would seem apparent, especially in instances of chronic pain, that a simple explanation like "arthritis" cannot adequately explain what is truly going on with a particular patient. While there very well may be biomechanical and physical issues like joint degeneration at play, to simplify a patient's suffering or pain to this one diagnosis is misguided.

And, what about patients who are experiencing real debilitating pain, but have no physical or biomechanical issues which can explain it? We've all seen patients in our clinics who have significant limitations or experienced pain but also have "negative imaging findings." Are these patients simply "making it up"? Is it "all in their head"?

I'd say that the answer to those questions above is a resounding, "No." But in order to understand why, we have to understand a few basic principles about all of the BSP factors that affect our health and well-being. These are the three basic principles of the BSP Model:

1. The relationship between psychological and physical factors of health can be extremely complex. A patient's subjective experience can result from physiological factors, but can't simply be reduced to them [1].
2. These different factors affect each individual differently, since we are dealing with this individual's subjective experience [1, 2].
3. Changes in one of these factors (biological, psychological, or social/environmental) potentially create real and notable changes in the other factor(s) [3].

Figure 1.1 illustrates the BSP Model and how different factors play a role in a patient's experience.

So, at the core of the BSP Model is the idea that each patient is uniquely different, experiencing a unique interplay between biological, psychological, and social/environmental factors. This means we can't treat every patient

Biopsychosocial model of healthcare

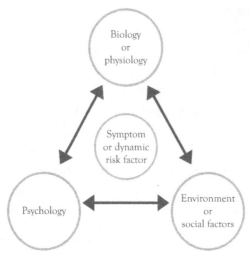

Figure 1.1 Illustration of biopsychosocial model

the same. We can't rely on rigid, cookie-cutter treatment approaches that are based on a diagnosis rather than the patient's unique experience.

It reminds me of a story I'm fond of telling. On my first day in an outpatient orthopedic rehab clinic, as a relatively new clinician, I was nervous. I felt that I didn't know the first thing about treating complex upper extremity diagnoses and injuries. Yet, there I was: at 07:45 am, looking at the chart of my first patient of the day, and reviewing the notes that the surgeon left for me. I was terrified.

Then one of the experienced therapists in that clinic put her arm around my shoulder. Then, as a southern lady from Tennessee, she leaned in and said with that comforting southern drawl that communicates calm and caring: "Now, honey. Just remember this: a shoulder is a shoulder is a shoulder. You treat 'em all like shoulders." I'm not going to lie: that advice gave me some confidence … for a little bit. But there was a problem: every shoulder I treated didn't seem to act like the shoulder I had treated before. In fact, sometimes a treatment technique or exercise that worked with one patient who had a shoulder injury simply didn't work with another shoulder. A technique or program that worked with one, didn't always work with another. I was getting mediocre outcomes.

Some patients got better, and some didn't. I started to search for solutions. That's when I began to read and learn about the BSP Model.

I then began to see the truth: that every patient is different. You can't treat them all the same just because they have the same diagnosis, injury, or surgery. A BSP approach to providing care considers the physical, psychological, and social factors of the disease or injury and promotes an integrated approach to treatment.

How did that change my treatment approach as a clinician? It made me look at each patient as a unique individual, with differing physical, psychological, and social factors affecting their condition. It made me leave behind the world of cookie-cutter treatment programs and rigid protocols. I was happy. My patients were happy. And most importantly, we (my patients and I) started seeing the outcomes we wanted.

Let's take a deeper look at the three different factors in the BSP Model and how they play a role in a patient's unique experience of an injury and their engagement in treatment.

Physical Factors

First up is the physical side of things. As clinicians, we all have a fairly good grasp on the physical factors that may adversely affect out patients' health, function, or pain. These may include acute injuries to the tissues, postural misalignment, arthrokinematic dysfunction, nerve damage, tissue lesions or lacerations, inflammation, and even weight/body type. All of these factors stem from biological or physiological roots, and they affect not only the function of the affected areas, but also a patient's psychosocial health.

In fact, something as simple as Body Mass Index (BMI); a physical factor has been shown to impact a patient's physical functioning and social functioning as well [4].

Given its prominence in the education of clinicians, and the fact that it seems easier to understand and grasp, clinicians tend to focus most of our evaluation and treatment efforts on the physical aspects of our patients' conditions. We take range of motion (ROM) measurements, complete strength assessments, palpate soft tissues, observe posture and motor patterns, complete manual therapy techniques, focus on exercises and stretches, and educate our patients on the importance of doing the exercises correctly.

All of this is important and necessary for effective evaluation and treatment, especially in cases of acute injuries or traumas. However, if we only go so far as the tissues, we potentially miss the other important aspects that can affect not only our patients' experience of pain or dysfunction, but also their response to treatment [3, 5].

Psychological Factors

The second set of factors in the BSP Model includes the psychological and/or cognitive factors at play. Since as early as the late 1970s, there has been an increasing focus on the role of human behavior and psychology play in determining our overall health and well-being. Up and to that point in time, the healthcare field had been based on the biomedical model of evaluation and treatment [6]. There are many reasons for this that involve in-depth discussions of the philosophical underpinnings of the culture and the times when the field of medicine and healthcare was born. Regardless of the reasons behind the focus on the biology of disease, the fact is that the healthcare field began focusing mainly on the physical aspects of disease and health.

This focus on the psychological factors of health and disease opens up an entire new world for both medical researchers and clinicians alike. For example, research has been published showing a direct relationship between a patient's cognition and physical abilities or performance [7].

As mentioned previously, to reduce a patient's condition, limitation, or dysfunction down to a "problem" with the tissues or body misses the great impact that the patient's psychological state and cognition has on their subjective experience of their condition.

Neurophysiology and the Neuroscience of Pain

As an example of the interplay between the psychological and biological factors that may affect a patient's daily routines, consider recent research of neuroscience education in patients with chronic pain. Recent evidence suggests that how we educate patients about their conditions and pain can have a real impact on clinical and performance outcomes.

Studies have shown that combining neuroscience education with traditional physical rehabilitation treatment can improve outcomes in patients with chronic low back pain (LBP) [3]. There is also evidence suggesting that approaching patient education nation from a purely biomechanical (biological) frame of reference may actually increase stress, anxiety, and even negatively impact clinical outcomes [8].

The important thing to remember here is that pain is always real. That can't be stated enough: pain is always real. Given what we know about the neuroscience of pain, we understand that pain is a protective mechanism of the brain. Essentially, the brain creates pain. Therefore, when a patient reports pain (even though they may have normal x-rays or imaging studies), the odds are very likely that they are truly experiencing pain. Acknowledging a patient's pain as real is the first step in building a strong therapeutic relationship.

Social Factors

After considering the physical and psychological factors affecting a patient, we must turn our attention to social and environmental factors that may be at play. The BSP Model is based on the understanding of the dynamic nature of differing factors that affect a patient's experience and ultimate outcomes. Social factors may impact a patient's behavioral response to physical conditions or symptoms [9]. This is largely due to the fact that sociocultural factors—beliefs about illness or treatment—can cause patients to think differently about their conditions, the efficacy of treatment, or even their willingness to participate.

Social learning impacts a patient's development of pain response behaviors, expression of pain, and even expectations of outcomes. How many times have you heard a patient say, "Well my neighbor (or cousin, aunt, etc.) had this [insert diagnosis/condition] and they never got better."? Studies have shown that physiological responses to pain can be conditioned by simply observing others in pain [9]. Taking that into consideration, you begin to understand the interaction between the physical, psychological, and social/environmental factors at play in a patient's experience of an injury or illness.

Social influences also affect the way families, community groups, and acquaintances interact with people experiencing chronic conditions, pain, or diseases. On top of that, ethnic expectations, cultural norms, and even sex and age stereotypes affect the patient-clinician relationship [9]. Starting as children, we learn socially appropriate—or acceptable— ways of reacting to and dealing with illness or pain. As an example, anyone with a toddler knows that young children experience minor falls, bumps, and bruises almost daily. How parents or adults respond to these minor injuries creates learning opportunities for how to ignore, respond to, or even over-respond to pain [9]. This can trigger operant learning mechanisms that can lead to the formation of chronic pain conditions.

All of this suggests that we as clinicians must understand any potential social or cultural influences that may be affecting a patient's experience of a given condition.

Clinical Application of the BSP Model

Alright, so now you hopefully have a better understanding of how physical, psychological, and social/environmental factors interact throughout a patient's experience of a disease, injury, or illness. But how does that change your treatment approach as a clinician? Let's take a brief look at how the BSP Model can be applied in a clinical setting, using a real-life example from my own clinical practice.

Mr. Smith and His Chronic Shoulder Pain

Mr. Smith was a middle-age man, a Vietnam veteran, and a former prisoner of war (POW). He was referred to my clinic, which was an out-patient specialty rehab and pain management clinic, with a diagnosis of "Chronic Right Shoulder Pain—Not Otherwise Specified" (How many times has a diagnosis like that come across your desk?). He had seen primary care, neurosurgery, orthopedics, pain management clinic, and even another physical therapy (PT) clinic in the VA system (Department of Veterans Affairs). He still experienced life-limiting shoulder pain. He showed up to his appointment with me late, disinterested, and clearly skeptical about what his outcomes would be.

Assessment

Firstly, an assessment or evaluation approach using the BSP Model as a guide emphasizes not only the biological or physical symptoms and factors, but also the patient's experiential perspective [10, 11]. So, that's exactly what I did with Mr. Smith. I looked at broader issues, not just the muscles and tissues of his shoulders. I probed into psychological and social components that were 100 percent unique to Mr. Smith. That meant that I had to select specific physical, psychological, behavioral, and cognitive measures to better understand his unique pain condition [10].

That's one thing I want to highlight: there is no definitive list of assessments to use. No one assessment or measure is inherently better than the next. And, while objective physical measures (ROM, MMT, etc.) are important and easier to track than subjective, self-reported measures, both need to be considered when using a BSP approach [10]. For example, as I mentioned earlier, the fear of movement or pain (or even lack of motivation) may affect the results of physical outcome measures [10]. So, the goal is to consider which assessments and measures will help provide you with a complete picture of that patient's unique condition and experience.

In Mr. Smith's case, I started with a step-by-step approach, starting with a general overview and evaluation of some potential precipitating factors (injury, tissues, posture, etc.) and then moved deeper into a more specific set of assessments looking at psychological and social factors as they presented themselves.

Outcome Measures

It seems like most clinicians, organizations, and payers require outcome measures that provide objective and measurable data. That's understandable, and we, as clinicians should strive to use outcome measures that we can also use to track progress, justify continued treatment, and show gains for reimbursement, value discussions, and so on.

When selecting measures to use in an assessment, try also to consider which measures will assimilate to a complete analysis of a patient's unique condition and experience. Put another way: try to pick different outcome measures that, when looked at together, provide a whole picture of the patient's situation.

So, in Mr. Smith's case, there were a few areas that I wanted to address. We obviously wanted to address the shoulder pain and functional limitations. So, we selected the QuickDASH (disabilities of the arm shoulder and hand) for the upper extremity (UE) limitations and pain. We also selected the Short-Form McGill Pain Questionnaire to assess the qualitative aspect (or lived experience) of the chronic shoulder pain. And, due to his history of post-traumatic stress disorder (PTSD) related to his experience as a POW, we selected the Traumatic Antecedents Questionnaire (TAQ). Those outcome measures and assessments, in conjunction with the standard ROM, manual muscle tests (MMT), and selected provocative tests, were able to provide a much more full and complete picture of Mr. Smith's unique situation and lived experience with his diagnosis of chronic shoulder pain.

Treatment Approaches

If you've been following along thus far, then you know that using a BSP approach acknowledges that there are too many factors at play for rigid treatment protocols or "cookie-cutter" treatment programs. Even if two patients are referred to your clinic with the same diagnosis, they each differ physically, socially, or even psychologically. Take Mr. Smith as an example. He not only had shoulder pain, but also a traumatic history that—even when working with the veteran population—may not be all too common in every other patient you may treat. Because of all these factors, which can be different with every patient, throwing these patients into the same exact treatment program will likely result in suboptimal outcomes [10].

I already mentioned my "a shoulder is a shoulder is a shoulder" story. And, I operated under that assumption for a while, achieving mediocre or average outcomes with my patients. I wondered why some patients got better very quickly, while others with the same diagnosis struggled to make even modest progress toward their treatment goals. It wasn't until I began to explore the application of a BSP approach to treatment that I began to see and experience the results both my clients and I wished for.

By addressing not simply the physical symptoms and issues with the patient's tissues, joints, and posture—and taking a broader look at each individual's context and situation—I was able to deliver a higher standard of care. This became most evident in treating patients, like Mr. Smith, who had been experiencing chronic pain for years; pain that was not just an issue with the tissues, but pain that was affected by psychological and social factors from his unique lived experience as a POW and combat veteran. Implementing some intervention strategies aimed at addressing those psychosocial factors allowed us to get to some of the "root" issues affecting Mr. Smith's lived experience of pain. For example, when he implemented some mind-body work and exercises, such as mindfulness, Mr. Smith gained the ability to address those underlying pain factors whenever they flared up. Now, while at the end of my time with Mr. Smith he was not completely pain-free, he was armed with the tools he would need to effectively manage his pain going into the future. And, in reality, that should be the goal of most healthcare services: to empower patients to become not only active participants in their care, but also become the "drivers" of their own health and well-being.

Patient Education and Engagement

On another, equally important note aside from treatment approaches, let's look at patient education. Throughout the treatment process, communication, instruction, and education between the clinician and the patient are vital to achieving the best outcomes possible. Since we are talking about the BSP Model, it should be apparent that each of these factors (physical, psychological, and social) are unique to each individual patient that we treat. There are many resources for methods and approaches to patient education, but regardless of the approach you choose, the goal should be to tailor it to each individual patient.

Engaging the patient throughout the treatment process also improves clinical outcomes. During initial interviews and assessments, asking open-ended questions and practicing active listening engages your patient and builds trust and rapport. You can use motivational interviewing as well to boost the patient's engagement and active participation in assessment and treatment. Increasing a patient's engagement in the evaluation and treatment process strengthens the therapeutic relationship between clinician and patient. It may lead to the patient becoming more open about other factors, which may be affecting recovery—such as family-related stress, work issues, or socioeconomic factors at play.

This not only improves clinical outcomes, but also improves the patient's overall experience in your clinic and with your services. Increasing patient engagement also improves patient retention. Increased patient retention improves your bottom line as a business owner, but it's also good for your patients, who will continue with a treatment program instead of dropping off partially through treatment. That means they get the maximum benefit of the plan of care you develop with and for them.

How BSP Factors Affect Patient Experience and Engagement

Ok, so we've covered a lot of information so far, and there's just one more piece I want to get to before moving on to Chapter 2 (are you still with me!?): The effect of the BSP Model on patient experience and engagement.

If we understand that a patient's experience—not only of treatment, but of the clinic or clinicians who treat them—is affected by physical, psychological, and social factors, it makes sense that we should take those into account when trying to create a positive patient experience. Clinic owners and healthcare facilities should take a look at their physical environments, processes, and staffing/personnel to ensure they are optimized to provide the best patient experience possible.

Physical Environments

The first thing that affects your patients when they arrive at your clinic or facility is the physical environment: the parking lot, entrance, and waiting areas. This includes the cleanliness, but is not limited to it. Of course, if the clinic is nasty, dusty, and smells of trash, you'll be starting in a hole as far as the patient experience goes, but other environmental factors can have just a large impact on a patient's experience.

For example, I'm sure nearly every clinic or facility—in the United States, anyways— is compliant with the American with Disabilities Act

(ADA) standards for accessibility. Let's consider that simply the baseline: widened doorways, ramps, handrails, accessible bathrooms, and so on. What about the layout of the building or clinic? Is it easy for a patient to navigate through, or are there hallways, doors, and turns that can be confusing? Consider the layout of the treatment space. When a patient comes in for treatment, can they stay in the same relative space, or do they need to be constantly shifted from area to area (mat over here, parallel bars at the far end of the clinic, assessment area in the other far corner)?

Noise level and the general atmosphere of a clinic or waiting area also impact a patient's experience. For example, loud radios, televisions, or other media devices in the waiting area or treatment space can impact a patient's ability to communicate with staff and clinicians. I remember a patient at the VA who became very agitated and upset because the television from the waiting area was so loud that he couldn't hear his therapist. He wore hearing aids and couldn't filter out the ambient noise. He ended up submitting a complaint to the department because of the poor experience. Situations like that truly have an impact not only on the patient's experience that day in the clinic, but they can also challenge the therapeutic relationship between patient and clinician.

Processes or "Touch Points"

Even before a patient arrives at your clinic or facility, odds are they have encountered a "touch point" that can set the tone for the rest of the patient engagement. Touch points can be anything from a phone call the patient receives after the clinic receives a referral, to preappointment paperwork or forms that are delivered to the patient ahead of their scheduled visit (not to mention the biggest touch point of all: the front desk—more on that later). If a patient has a negative experience when trying to schedule their initial appointment, for example, they arrive at the clinic with some negative feelings or expectations about the visit. They may take a less active role in the initial assessment, be more skeptical of advice given, or be generally less willing to participate in a prolonged plan of care.

The biggest, and most frequently encountered, touch point is the front desk. Often, front desk staff and business managers in therapy clinics interact well with patients and their families. They are helpful, kind, and courteous. But what about front desk procedures such as sign-in, scheduling, or payment processes? Sometimes, seemingly small nuances or procedures can negatively impact a patient's experience. In instances involving minor procedural pinch-points, it helps if everyone staffing the front desk has a higher purpose in mind.

We all went into healthcare because we want to help people get better, whether it be by relieving their pain or helping them meet developmental milestones. Sometimes for staff however, it can easily become just a job and procedures that could be set aside to make the patient's experience more convenient or pleasurable become iron-clad laws that cannot be broken. When staff and clinicians buy in to a higher purpose, or mission, of the clinic or organization, procedures and rules can be bent, bypassed, or changed to make the patient's experience the best it can be.

Social and Interpersonal Interactions

As mentioned up above, staff interactions with patients provide the biggest opportunity to positively impact the patient experience. They also have the ability to do the opposite. The way staff communicates with patients signals to them—either consciously or subconsciously—how to perceive the forthcoming experience in a clinic. When a patient checks in for their first appointment, are they seemingly shuffled along the "check-in" process, filling out paperwork, handing over their insurance card, and so on? Obviously, we need to check patients in and verify identity and coverage, but *how* do we go about it? A disinterested receptionist shuffling patients through what feels like a conveyor belt check-in process gives patients the subtle sign that they are just a number in the system. It prompts them to expect nothing more than impersonalized, generic care even if that's not the case. A patient with this perception may feel like they are getting run through a canned exercise program in the clinic, even if the therapist has individualized it and is monitoring and progressing the patient on an individual basis.

Another example involves how our clinic staff address patients. Something as simple as calling a patient by their name, or remembering their name when they call back or return to the clinic, greatly improves the patient's perception of their experience. Patients want to feel valued, heard, and listened to. Recent studies suggest that patients want to be involved in decision making and act as partners in both the quality and improvement of the healthcare services they receive [6]. That all starts with being *identified* as a unique individual receiving care in this clinic or facility.

Personalization is one of the most effective ways of making a patient feel valued and heard. An opportunity to improve personalization occurs with patient education. Especially when treating patients in pain or with chronic conditions, patient education takes a central role in the treatment process. Therapists and clinics that understand the BSP factors that may be at play in a particular patient's situation are able to tailor the education and information they provide the patient. This makes the information more relevant to the patient and also gives the patient the sense that this clinic or clinician truly cares about them and their situation.

Summary

At the end of the day, this is really only a 30,000-foot view of the BSP Model of healthcare and how it can be applied to a rehabilitation setting. Over the last 50 or so years, entire books and programs have been written and developed focusing entirely on this model of healthcare delivery. It's not something that you become great at after reading a brief chapter in a book. But you can begin implementing pieces of it in everyday practice. For example, simply becoming aware of the psychological and social factors that may be affecting a patient's physical condition will make you more aware of potential complications. It can also help you strengthen and improve the therapeutic relationship you develop with patients.

Patients know when they are being put through a cookie-cutter exercise or treatment program. They don't like it. They also know when the clinician they are seeing takes the time to learn about their individual and specific issue and circumstances. Sometimes, all you need to do to greatly increase a patient's outcomes is take the time to listen to them. When patients feel listened to, understood, and engaged, they take a more active role in their treatment program, which is what every clinician should want. We want patients to come to our clinics, actively participate in treatment, and continue with their programs and improvements long after they leave our clinics. Applying a BSP approach to assessment and treatment can help make this a reality.

In the end, improving patient experience and engagement in your clinics and facilities requires a comprehensive review of everything from our physical environments to staff training and interaction. You need to understand that patients want to be listened to and valued as partners in their healthcare. You should try and implement procedures and processes to foster this partnership with your patients. Understanding how BSP factors can affect the patient experience helps you modify and change as needed to deliver care that is truly focused on each individual patient that comes into your clinics. Because at the end of the day, that is what healthcare and rehabilitation are all about: the patient.

If you'd like to learn more about the BSP Model, or if you'd like to see where I pulled all the information for this chapter from, check out the references listed at the end of this book.

CHAPTER 2

Commitment #2

Build Meaningful Relationships

We will prioritize improving our interpersonal skills and abilities and focus on building meaningful relationships with each patient; relationships built on trust, empathy, and care.

It goes without saying that—at the very least—patients expect to be treated by clinicians who are professional, competent, friendly, and caring. Research also shows that patients place a great deal of weight on the clinician's ability to communicate effectively; from explaining a diagnosis to educating the patient on self-management strategies [1]. In fact, this research concludes that high-quality patient–clinician interactions are more important to patients than convenient clinic locations, parking, organization of care, and even, in some cases, the treatment outcome.

Given that information, we as clinicians and clinic owners should try to do anything we can to improve the interactions that patients have with our staff and clinicians. This starts with the way the clinician communicates, including language, word choice, body language, and active listening.

Healthcare is a personal service involving a human experience. Patients want that experience. They want to feel that their clinician understands their situation, knows how to help, and truly cares about them.

The best clinicians—those who are sought out by patients—are those who are able to make that human connection felt. To do that, you need to become adept at cultivating meaningful patient relationships.

How Important Are Strong Patient Relationships? The Business Reasons to Focus Here

There's a common problem in the healthcare field; especially in the physical rehabilitation and therapy space where I work. That problem falls under the category of *not enough patients*. The more clinic owners and managers I talk to and work with, the more often I notice this pattern: Owners and managers see falling numbers (revenue, referrals, appointments, etc.). They feel the pressure (to make payroll or hit their departmental numbers). They become desperate for more patients. This leads them to run to the only thing they believe will help them: lead generation.

OK, in the healthcare field, we call it *drumming up referrals*; but, it's the same thing. As I often find in my work with clients, referral problems (or "not-enough-patient-problems") may actually be *patient retention* problems. Unfortunately, the best marketing plan in the world fails if it doesn't consider the **patient relationship cycle**.

Managing Patient Relationships

Let's take a look at what happens when the census dips or the clinic schedule becomes light.

Managers and clinic owners see lower revenue and dips in appointment scheduling as a *referral* problem. "If only we could get doctor X to refer a few more patients ..." or "We really need to develop relationships with some other referral partners ...." These phrases usually precede the implementation of some sort of new, growth-hack-related, marketing plan or system. And, it works ... for a little while. Referrals increase. Clinicians end up with full schedules again, and all seems right in the world. Then, usually 6 to 12 months later, it happens again. Numbers start dipping. Schedules free up, and clinicians are treating less.

What happened? The marketing plan worked. You saw an increase in referrals and appointments being scheduled. You may have even considered hiring staff to handle the new workload—and to treat the number of patients surely coming down the pipe. Within a year or two, you're looking at the same problem. But why?

It all stems from not understanding, or capitalizing on, how the patient relationship cycle works.

Patient Relationships

As in most service-based fields, healthcare ultimately revolves around relationships. Relationships between patients and their clinicians can impact everything from clinical outcomes to satisfaction ratings [1]. But, what is a patient–clinician relationship?

Well, as in every other human relationship, patient–clinician relationships form through social interactions between the clinician and the patient. Communication, for one, plays a large role in developing these relationships. How a clinician speaks, asks questions, and displays body language impacts the trust and confidence that a patient feels.

Oftentimes, this relationship forms "on the fly." Clinics and clinicians don't intentionally try and form strong patient relationships. I always say that people who choose healthcare as a career (or calling) are naturally skilled at interpersonal communication and relationship building. This means that most of the time, clinicians are able to form relatively strong and meaningful relationships with their patients. The patients, in turn, trust their clinicians and can actively engage in the planning, execution, and benchmarking throughout their treatment.

Sometimes, however, clinicians are busy. They feel rushed. They're under pressure to meet certain productivity metrics. They fall into a rhythm of "conveyor belt" healthcare. They treat patient appointments like checkboxes that need to be ticked in order to do their job, make their boss happy, and get paid. If you think about it, it's not their fault. They're in an environment where time-based productivity runs the show.

Whether you work in the outpatient rehab world, or private practice like a family medicine clinic, it can feel that your whole day consists of trying to treat patients enough to get results, get your documentation done, and meet productivity. In environments like that, it becomes more important to intentionally cultivate strong patient relationships.

Cultivating Strong Patient Relationships

So, if strong patient–clinician relationships are important, how do we go about developing them? Ultimately, relationships between clinicians and patients develop in the daily and routine interactions between them. How a clinician greets a new patient, or how that clinician conducts the initial assessment or interview sets the tone for the relationship.

The patient receives subtle cues from the clinician during these initial interactions.

What information are they focused on? What do they care about? Are they looking more at their watch or computer screen than me?

We may not be aware of it, but all of those little things can either build or detract from a strong patient relationship.

Depending on your setting, population, and area of specialty, patient relationships can be difficult to form. For example, I once worked covering some acute care caseload for the hospital to which my outpatient rehab clinic was attached. I saw patients for an initial assessment, made some discharge recommendations, and then they left the hospital in the next day or two. While you can still develop good working patient–clinician relationships, under those circumstances, it can be challenging.

Ultimately, our aim as clinicians should be to communicate to our patients an attitude of care, empathy, and sincerity. We want our patients to know that we don't merely see them as a number (or four billable units), but as real people experiencing real dysfunctions or limitations. We want to cultivate an environment of safety, trust, and collaboration. While we need to check certain boxes and gather important information to do our job properly, we also need to be aware of the social and emotional role we as clinicians play in the healthcare process. Patient education and counseling, responding to patient emotions, and even simply providing an empathetic ear or sounding board play just as important a role in healthcare as gathering accurate ROM, manual muscle tests (MMT), or other diagnostic data.

The Patient Relationship Cycle

Understanding the importance of cultivating strong patient–clinician relationships leads to some questions. One of these questions revolves around the cycle of patient–clinician interaction. Did you ever think about the life cycle of a patient's interaction with you or your clinic?

Patients start off as new referrals or prospective patients and, through their interactions with us and our clinics, develop relationships with clinicians, staff members, and even our organization. Understanding where patients may be on this cycle helps clinics and organizations intentionally build strong relationships with their patients.

Enter what I call the **patient relationship cycle**.

This cycle (Figure 2.1) represents the typical life cycle of a patient's interaction and relationship with your clinic. It begins with a new referral—or, in some cases, a piece of marketing—and ends with (hopefully) a returning patient who actively refers friends, relatives, and neighbors to your clinic. Your communication and interaction with a patient should correspond to the stage that they are in.

New Referral

Whether a patient is referred to your clinic by another medical provider, or if they hear about you through your marketing, odds are that most of your prospective patients in the area (your ideal patients) start their relationship with you before you even see them. Your reputation—usually conveyed by the referring provider or referring acquaintance (like a neighbor or friend)—influences the patient's perception of you, your clinic,

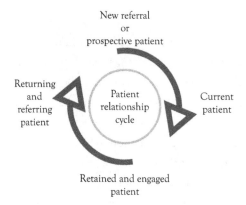

Figure 2.1 The patient relationship cycle

and the quality of your services. Likewise, your marketing and messaging subtly communicate to your prospective clients about those same things. These patients and prospective patients begin forming an idea in their minds about you, your clinic, and your services—all without even meeting you.

When these patients show up at your clinic for an initial appointment, free consultation, or evaluation, they bring with them these perceptions and preconceived ideas. That means when patients are in this stage of their relationship with you and your clinic, you need to be proactive and intentional in your communication with them. This may mean providing referral sources with information or "talking points" about you. Sometimes, having brochures available in the offices of your major referral sources also helps. When crafting marketing messages, be sure that those messages communicate what you want to convey to those prospective patients. This may be the value you bring to the table, social proof by way of testimonies, the fact that you are experts in your specialization, and so on.

Then, when this patient walks into your clinic for their first appointment, you need to make good on those promises you've made in your messages and marketing. Your front-office staff should also be involved in this, as they are likely the first people your patients see, talk to, and interact with. As I've found working with clients, oftentimes the process of care (on-boarding, new patient paperwork) influences patient engagement and experience as much as the actual care they receive.

Current Patient

Once a patient takes the step to schedule a follow-up appointment, the communication and interaction change again. These patients are no longer "prospects." You don't need to convince them to schedule that first appointment or interaction (you're over that hill), but you do need to provide them with reasons to become engaged in the treatment. Active patient engagement and participation positively impact both clinical outcomes and patient satisfaction scores. So, how do you get a patient actively engaged in the treatment process?

Hopefully, at the first appointment, you or your clinician(s) took time to listen to the patient, validate their experiences, and answer their questions in a way that communicated empathy, understanding, and competence.

After that, the next step is to seek input from the patient in the treatment planning process. Focusing on goals and objectives that are meaningful to the patient leads to greater engagement and experience. That may mean regular "check-in" conversations between the clinician and the patient.

Sometimes, even the clinic owner or manager can take a random stroll through the clinic and waiting area and ask patients: "Are we doing everything that you expect or desire to help your recovery?" or "Is there anything we can do to better help you meet your goals?" Taking the time to ask these questions really makes an impact on patients' perspectives of the clinic.

It is also important to note that, just because a patient schedules a follow-up visit (or two or three) doesn't mean you're out of the woods. As we'll discuss in Chapter 5, many patients never make it out of this stage. They go from current patients to "where-did-they-go" patients. Oftentimes, a low patient retention rate may result from a breakdown in the patient's relationship—either with the clinician or the clinic/organization. We need to make sure that we never take our current patients for granted. We must always take steps to ensure that they're engaged and satisfied (and if not, figure out how to fix it).

Retained Patient

So, a patient has stuck with you past the first few follow-up appointments, now what? At this point in the patient relationship, the clinic and clinician need to focus on *engagement (again, we'll cover this in Chapter 5)*. Up to this point, your patient was exposed to your message or reputation. They've interacted with your staff and clinicians. And— hopefully—they've participated in developing their treatment plan and desired goals, and expressed their aspirations for treatment. Now, you and your clinic need to use that information and integrate it into that patient's treatment and appointments.

Take the time to gauge how the patient feels about the progress of treatment, the relevance of treatment, and their progress toward their desired goals. Use that information to inform treatment appointments. It's one thing to ask a patient about how they feel about treatment. But, you take it to a whole new level when you actually *act* on the information and feedback the patient provides. When the patient feels valued, heard, listened to, and feels like a partner in their treatment plan, they naturally become more motivated and engaged in treatment.

That leads to **course of care retention** (retaining a patient through to completing their plan of care). This should be one of the few key metrics that you focus on regularly, as it shows the level of patient engagement and satisfaction with your clinic and services. Patients who are engaged and are having good experiences in your clinic are more likely to finish their course of care. If you notice low numbers with plan of care completion, take a close look at patient engagement and experience.

Returning and Referring Patient

Aside from course of care retention, another form of retention is just as important: **clinic retention**. This type of retention leads to repeat patients. These patients may have come to your clinic for shoulder pain. They had a great experience, felt engaged in treatment, met their goals, and completed their plan of care. Now, perhaps they have elbow pain or hand pain. They choose to return to your clinic (because they had such a great experience the last time). Now, obviously, we hope that our patients complete their plan of care in our clinics and then go on to live a long, pain-free life. But, if they're in a position where they need services again, we want them to think of us first, right?

Another side benefit of getting a patient to this stage of the patient relationship cycle impacts business growth: *word-of-mouth referrals.* Oftentimes, patients who choose to return to your clinic feel so good about the services and treatment you provide that they tell their friends, neighbors, and relatives about your clinic. They become advocates— and, in some cases, fans—of your clinicians and your clinic. If they were referred to you by another healthcare provider, they'll go back to that provider and talk about the great experience they had in your clinic. This may influence that provider's choice to send more referrals your way.

Oftentimes, I notice that clinics simply hope, pray, and trust that their patients will come back to their clinic in the future. They know these patients had great experiences, realized their goals, and left happy. But, they still wonder whether these patients will come back to their clinic if they need services in the future. This typically results from not having a good method for follow-up and engagement of these patients. Whether it be via social media, e-mail marketing, or phone calls (yes, people still talk on the phone), you need to have some way of both following up with former patients and maintaining that relationship (Figure 2.2).

The Patient Relationship Cycle and Implications

It's easy to see falling numbers, fewer appointments, and less patients as a lead generation (or referral) problem. In some cases, you may be right. Oftentimes, however, you need to take a look at metrics and data that speak to patient *engagement and retention*. Low numbers in the areas of plan of care completion, returning patients, and canceled appointments/ no-shows indicate problems in the patient relationship cycle. Understanding this cycle is the key for any clinic owner or manager to increase retention, engagement, and returning patients.

If you go and spend thousands of dollars on marketing campaigns aimed at boosting referrals and new appointments, you will see an increase in new appointments and referrals. You'll notice revenue increases. What you may not notice is the slow, continuous leak of patients *not* coming back, finishing their plans of care, or referring friends to your clinic. At the end of the day, lead generation (or drumming up referrals) *covers up* problems with patient experience, engagement, and retention. Basically,

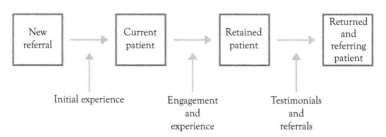

Figure 2.2 Patient relationships

if you're spending money to fill up a leaky bucket, you'll find out that your bucket ends up empty at the end of the day.

Offering High-Impact, High-Value Services Through Relationships

So, the question arises: *how do you deliver high-value, high-impact services to patients in a way that values their unique circumstances and builds strong, meaningful relationships?*

Now, that is the million-dollar question.

Here is how I advise my clients and staff on that topic. Now, this comes from my work as a consultant, helping to manage integrated clinical support services for the Georgia Department of Behavioral Health and Developmental Disabilities, my work involving relationship-based care at the Department of Veterans Affairs, and my work helping private healthcare organizations develop systems to maximize patient engagement and retention.

It all boils down to this: delivering high-value, high-impact services. Healthcare is changing rapidly, and the move to value-based reimbursement and the like drives much of the conversation on the part of healthcare administrators and policy makers. Payers and policy makers are noticing the benefits of leveraging technology to improve access, decrease cost, and improve outcomes across the continuum of care.

That being said, you can't simply use "standard" clinical practices and procedures and expect things to go well. The change in the healthcare landscape and context, as well as patient and client expectations, all dictate that you learn to take your highest-value services and treatment techniques and adapt them for the demands of the future.

This involves addressing patient expectations, moving toward self-management techniques for treatment, highlighting patient education and empowerment, and realizing that one of our greatest assets as clinicians and healthcare professionals is our vast clinical and professional knowledge. That means that the greatest way to create a lasting impact on our patients' lives involves leveraging our knowledge, through the relationship we form with our patients, and guiding them to become the drivers of their own health and well-being.

Let's start with addressing patient expectations.

Expectations

Oftentimes, patient expectations about the type of treatment they'll receive impacts their experience in your clinic.

What do I mean by that?

Well, how many patients have you seen in your clinic that expect you to "do" something to/for them to relieve their symptoms? Just give me a pill, crack my joint, massage this muscle, stretch me here ... the list goes on and on. The problem with these expectations stems from an underlying, and misinformed view of healthcare and what healthcare treatment should be.

As I discussed in Chapter 1, for the vast majority of medical history, we relied on a biomedical model of treatment. This model rests on the idea that injury, illness, or disease stems from biological or anatomical dysfunctions. It doesn't consider the social, environmental, and even psychological factors that can be at play in a patient's specific situation.

Sometimes, either in clinic or over the web, or in virtual spaces, your patients may hold many expectations and beliefs about treatment based on this biomedical model. Your goal should be to provide education and communicate in a way that is not only both empathetic and understanding but also reframes their expectations about treatment, outcomes, and recovery.

This often involves a discussion about the difference between active and passive treatments. The literature shows that true, high-value treatment is based on active treatments (self-management skills, mindfulness, active movement, etc.) and provides better long-term clinical outcomes than passive treatments (medications, manual therapy, injections, etc.) [2]. While some of these passive treatments may be required to help a patient overcome an injury or dysfunction, long-term improvement hinges on that patient's ability to self-manage their condition after the initial treatment has ended.

Especially with new technologies improving access and allowing us to interact with patients in the virtual space, you must reframe patient expectations about the value of active treatments, because passive treatments can't easily be delivered or provided through a screen.

Facilitating Self-Management

As mentioned previously, self-management skills and techniques provide better long-term outcomes than passive treatments [2]. I'm not saying there's anything wrong with passive treatments, especially if used in a way to encourage or facilitate participation in active treatment. But, I am suggesting that the core components of treatment plans should be based on providing patients with the skills, techniques, and strategies to manage their own health and recovery.

This focus achieves two goals: (1) it empowers your patient to become the driver of their own health and well-being and (2) it decreases clinician (or medical) dependence. It also fundamentally alters the relationship you have with your patients.

No longer are you the person who can put their back "into alignment" or "adjust" their neck, or "massage" their sore muscles (or provide any other specific, passive treatment). Taking a self-care and self-management approach to treatment, you become a guide and trusted resource to your patient, who is now motivated and taking control of their own health. They become actively engaged in their own care.

Your patients begin looking at you as a coach or accountability partner, as well as a trusted adviser on matters related to their health (not just the diagnosis that originally brought them to your clinic).

Patient Education

Continuing on with the theme of active versus passive treatment, and delivering high-value care via telehealth, you must consider patient education. The type of education you provide to your patients should "facilitate active engagement approaches (targeted exercise therapy, physical activity, and healthy lifestyle habits) and reduce reliance on passive interventions" [3]. You can see a theme forming here, right?

If self-management, active treatment, and the like offer the highest form of value to patients, then you should educate your patients with that type of information. Especially in the virtual or hybrid healthcare environment, where a patient might not "see the point" of attending if you can't physically touch or feel the area of pain or dysfunction, you must address these expectations through proper education at the outset of assessment and treatment.

Patient education also helps you reframe patient expectations about treatment, potential outcomes, and the benefits of services. Your greatest asset as a healthcare professional is your vast knowledge and experience. The way you deliver that knowledge and experience to your patient and their unique situation impacts their view of treatment and expectations for recovery, and can encourage them to take a more active role in their own health.

Encouragement, Coaching, and Empowerment

Unfortunately, many clients and patients that show up at clinics across the country tend to value short-term relief at the cost of long-term outcomes. This, again, refers to the seemingly universal desire on the part of patients to receive some treatment or intervention. This is likely due to the fact that, at least for the vast majority of the healthcare industry's existence, clinicians and organizations have reinforced the idea that passive treatments are the standards of care [2].

Simply put: most patients that walk into your clinic expect you to do something for/to them to relieve their pain, take away their symptoms or dysfunction, and so on.

That's one reason why taking an educational, empathic, and encouraging approach to patient care plays a vital role in helping improve outcomes, engagement, and satisfaction scores. You must address a patient's expectations early, at the beginning. You should use education as a tool to help patients understand that your ultimate goal is to help them overcome whatever limitation, pain, or symptoms they are currently experiencing by giving them the resources, skills, and support necessary to do so on their own.

You can certainly use passive treatment modalities as an adjunct to active treatments, self-management, and the like. But, your patients need to understand that your role in the healthcare process is to provide the necessary encouragement, support, and assistance to empower them to take control of their own health and well-being.

Remember: You're a coach, a mentor, a guide; not a handyman or Mr. Fix-it.

Building Long-Term Relationships

One of the many benefits of taking this approach to healthcare service delivery becomes apparent over the course of care, and then in returning patients: real, lasting relationships with your patients and clients. When passive treatment modalities remain the core service offered at your clinic, the interaction you have with your patients stays at a merely transactional level. The patient comes in. You do your thing. They feel better and leave. They come may or may not come back again, depending on how they're feeling. That's it.

Now, I always say that clinicians that get into this field typically possess great people skills. They build relationships easily, are warm, welcoming, and inviting; and their patients genuinely value the relationship they have with them. However, this relationship oftentimes stays at a superficial level. They may open up about their shoulder pain, how it's impacting their day-to-day living, and their hopes for recovery. They may even share about their family, social life, and so on. But, when the focus of the interaction is on this "pain" or "symptom," the relationship doesn't grow deep roots.

However, when the focus of the interaction is on empowering your patient to take the driver's seat in their own health and well-being, the relationship blossoms. No longer are your appointments and interactions simply transactional.

You now become a trusted adviser, mentor, coach, or whatever term you like. You become the trusted guide, helping your patient achieve their ultimate goal of a full and healthy life.

That means you see a greater impact in your work, your patients value you more, and you build long-lasting relationships with them. They'll not only think of you the next time their shoulder hurts, but they'll also think of you when they have some health or lifestyle change they want to pursue.

It also means that you end up having more meaningful and deep conversations about their health and situations. It also means that, sometimes, you end up needing to have difficult conversations with them about lifestyle habits or misguided or misinformed expectations (more on that in the coming chapters). But, when you take the time to form real, long-lasting relationships with your patients, you find that, even when confrontation arises, the benefits outweigh any discomfort or emotional stress that comes from "real" relationships.

CHAPTER 3

Commitment #3

Put People Ahead of Policies

We will put people ahead of procedures and policies.

I once worked for the Department of Veterans Affairs (VA) in an outpatient clinic at a VA medical center. This environment, in particular, highlighted one of the major issues in healthcare today: we tend to prioritize policies and procedures over people. Part of that stems from our biomedical history, as well as the environment of efficiency and productivity in which healthcare now finds itself. When everything is a number, a unit, or a line on a spreadsheet, it's easy to make decisions without considering the impact they will have on the real people on the other end.

Take, for example, blanket requirements or protocols (we were fond of those at the VA). If you run the numbers and determine that X percent of patients with diagnosis Y successfully manage the diagnosis or recover after completing a certain treatment, it's very easy to make the blanket policy that every patient with diagnosis Y should complete that treatment first. On paper, it looks great. You can make projections and calculate recovery rates, costs, and the like. However, blindly applying that policy to every patient with diagnosis Y fails to consider the individual circumstances or factors that may make that treatment ineffective for that patient.

Many patients are stuck in treatment plans which aren't appropriate because some bureaucrat somewhere made a blanket policy about their diagnosis, and now the patient—not the bureaucrat—suffers as a result of that policy.

Now, this is an example of how the process of care or policy steamrolled many patients. It happened because the organization took a facility-centered approach or mindset while developing policies. It forgot to take a patient-centered approach. This led to many policies and procedures put in place that look good on paper, but fail to account for the uniqueness of each patient's situation.

Processes and Procedures

Besides large, organization-level policies, simple day-to-day processes also affect patient engagement and experience.

Whether you run an outpatient orthopedic clinic or a home health-care agency, improving patient experience and engagement is always a priority. There are many points along a patient life cycle (see how we're building on previous chapters) that have the ability to either add to or detract from a patient's total experience in your clinic or facility. Often, these "touch points" appear rather benign and harmless; but taken in totality, they have far-reaching effects on how our patients perceive the quality and ultimate value of the care we provide.

So, what is a touch point?

A touch point is any area that you, your clinic, or staff interact with a patient or potential patient. From the first phone call to the last treatment and from the first advertisement to the last piece of communication, these interactions make up what we refer to as the *patient experience*. Sometimes, we nail it. At other times, we walk away wondering *how the heck did that go so badly?*

Some patients leave our clinics in a great mood, ready to tell everyone they know how great our clinic, services, and team are. Others leave our clinics apathetic at best—if they even complete their plan of care—without anything notable to say. They may not have had a negative experience, but they definitely didn't experience anything to write home about either. Most of the time, this hit-or-miss we experience with patient experience results from not fully understanding *where* along the patient life cycle a problem occurred. That's what we'll look at here.

Common Touch Points That Affect Patient Experience

As mentioned earlier, any place or area that you, your clinic, or your staff interact with a patient or potential patient is considered a touch point. Sometimes, it's easy to see a problem along the timeline of a patient engagement and know how to fix it. In other instances, the issue may be much more nuanced and difficult to diagnose.

In these situations, it helps to try and make a list of every area where a patient or potential patient may come in contact with you, your clinic, or your employees to try and narrow down the focus. Let's look at some common touch points for every clinic and how they may negatively impact patient experience. Of course, you could (and should) also use surveying to find the biggest areas of frustration and work to build a culture that values the patient experience. The key to this is to always take a patient-centered approach when developing the processes at your facility or organization.

Referral and On-Boarding Process

What is the process for on-boarding new patients at your clinic?

This touch point generates many complaints from patients who find tedious and complex on-boarding processes unnecessary, at best, and down-right annoying, at worst. Insurance verification, primary care provider (PCP) referrals, and the like are necessary parts of bringing new patients into your clinic. But if you're not careful, your on-boarding process can turn an opportunity to impress into a liability for complaints and frustration.

Preappointment Packets

Take the preappointment paperwork (or, as some call it: "new-patient packets") as an example. Everything from the format, to directions, and to apparent redundancies provides an opportunity to improve patient engagement and experience.

Are new patients providing this paperwork in advance of their appointment, or do they spend the first 15 to 20 minutes of an initial appointment filling out paperwork? If the latter applies to new-patient packets or paperwork, odds are that the evaluating clinician doesn't have adequate time to review it before the patient is sitting in front of them. I can tell you this: if there's one thing that frustrates new patients, it's the feeling that the clinician hasn't taken the time to review any paperwork or history before seeing them.

Think about it. Why would you have a patient fill out an entire packet of past medical history, procedures, surgeries, and so on only to have them retell all of that information a few minutes later when they're seen by a clinician? If you can change this process so that the patient fills this packet out ahead of time—even better, submitting it electronically to the clinic—and giving the clinician time to review it before they arrive, you greatly improve the experience for both the patient and the clinician. The patient feels that the clinic is truly prepared and invested in their issue or dysfunction, and the clinician doesn't feel like they're "winging" it with every new patient. It's a win-win.

Communication

Communicating with current patients can be difficult, especially when instances like cancellations, emergencies, or clinic closures occur with little notice. But the manner and method in which we communicate with patients open the door for outstanding experiences. A well-thought-out communication strategy and method engages patients and makes them feel valued and cared for. Let's just break down two main parts of how we communicate with patients: the method and the manner (style).

Method

One of the first decisions we make when it comes to communicating with patients is the method we choose to use. So many options exist today, and the acceleration of technological advancement means more options become available with increasing regularity. With so many options, selecting a communication method can be overwhelming.

When selecting which method your clinic uses to communicate with patients, take into consideration patient demographics, desires, and values.

For example, if the majority of your patients are elderly, do not like using computers, and value personal interaction, then maybe moving all patient communications to a cloud-based secure messaging system isn't the way to go.

Given the advancement in technology, it may be beneficial to adopt a blended model for communicating with patients.

Some clinics I have worked for have used this method with good results. Offering the patients a choice of how they receive communication from your clinic makes them feel heard and improves their experience by allowing them to participate in the patient–clinic relationship. As I've often said, patients want to act as partners in their healthcare programs and plans. This extended to little decisions like how they communicate with their clinics or clinicians.

Style

The style or manner in which you communicate with patients also sends subtle cues that can impact the patient experience. This applies to clinic communications like call-backs, scheduling, and the like, and it also applies to in-person communication. How we say things to patients matters almost as much—if not more—than *what* we say.

Take, for example, a patient in pain. As we have written about here, a patient's condition or diagnosis is affected not only by the physical or biological components at play, but also by psychological and social factors. When a patient describes their pain or limitations, how you reply sends subtle cues that can potentially have a negative impact on their experience in your clinic. For example, if you say to a patient: "I know this pain feels real to you"; what the patient hears is: "but it's not real for me." Saying things like this to patients automatically undermines the therapeutic relationship. How will a patient trust you if they don't think you even believe what they are saying to you? How do you think that affects their experience and engagement during treatment, throughout their plan of care, and ultimately when they leave your clinic?

Even when our communication is not face to face or in person, *how* we structure it says a lot to patients. There is always a fine line between communicating in a way that is understandable, clear, and accurate compared to coming across as complex, dull, and dry. Going back to using emotional language here makes a big difference. What emotional outcome do you want your communication to elicit in your patients? Do you want them to feel empowered, inspired, or motivated? Structuring your communication in a way that gets the information across and engages patients is the key to using communication to improve patient experience.

Check-In Process

As you will likely discover when making your list of touch points, the front desk is a hub for patient touch points. Front office staff and receptionists are usually the first people from the clinic your patients speak with and they're also generally the last. That's why it's so important to hire the right people, train them appropriately, and work to build a culture in your clinic that puts the patient first. When everyone is on the same page with patient experience and engagement, a lot of these issues can be dealt with quickly and with little drama.

Just to cover one of the many front desk touch points, let's look at check-in procedures. When a patient comes to the clinic for an appointment, what does the check-in process look like? Are the directions clear and understandable? What is the average wait time?

Some things like wait times can fluctuate, especially in cases where patients show up late, an emergency arises, or a clinician calls in for the day. Even if wait times are on the longer side, *how* this is communicated to the patients by front desk staff can make all the difference between a good experience and a complaint. If a clinician is running behind, the front desk staff can inform the patient as they check-in of the delay and then take a few extra seconds to explain how the clinic values one-on-one care and works to make sure that every patient receives individual attention from clinicians. Now this will fall on deaf ears if those statements aren't backed up in practice. Patients can tell the difference between a clinic that is really trying to provide great individualized care and one that is just saying what it has to as an excuse for wait times or other inefficiencies.

Financial Obligations and Expectations

As healthcare changes, especially in the United States, more and more patients are becoming more aware of the costs associated with receiving treatment. Rising premiums, deductible costs, and copays drive patients to question whether receiving treatment is worth the cost.

The best way to address this concern, while also building trust with patients, is to be as open and up-front about the costs of treatment. For some clinics who have moved to a cash-based model, conversations about cost and expenses are becoming easier. For other clinics that may still be relying on third-party reimbursement and patients who are not used to paying higher costs out of pocket, it takes some practice. As a general rule, you should always try to get at least an estimated cost per visit to the patient *before* their first visit in the clinic.

Nothing can turn a good experience sour quite as fast as a patient being told that they owe much more than they anticipated for their visit. There is something in behavioral economics/psychology called the peak-end rule that says people's memories of past experiences are not related to the average level of positive or negative feelings [1]. Rather, their memories are related to the extreme point and the end of that experience [2].

So, think of this: a patient goes to PT, completes 12 sessions, and meets their goals. They are feeling great at their last appointment. Then a few days or weeks later, they get *huge* bill from that clinic. What do you think happens to this patient's memory of your clinic and services? They may say something like: "**Ya**, they did an alright job, but they were way too expensive." That result can be avoided simply by being open and up-front about costs.

I've heard of a few clinics that will schedule an appointment with a patient and then verify their insurance to get an estimated cost. They will then call the patients back a few days before their appointment and inform them of the costs. Taking this extra step lets patients know that your clinic truly cares about their cost of attending treatment.

Going a step further, clinicians should be able to have discussions with patients about the length of treatment programs and how that affects the cost. There were many times when I as a clinician had conversations with patients who revolved around collaboratively structuring a treatment program that would help the patient achieve their goals at the lowest cost to them. These conversations left patients feeling valued and cared for. They were more compliant with home programs and very engaged during in-clinic treatment sessions. They also left great reviews and testimonials about the clinic and how the staff really looked out for them.

Example: A Patient-First Approach to On-Boarding

Now all of this sounds great and even idealistic. But, how can you concretely implement these concepts in your day-to-day operations?

To answer that question, I'm going to share with you a simple process for on-boarding new patients at your clinic, department, or organization. I call it a bottom-up approach to patient on-boarding; a truly patient-first approach, if you would.

Think about the last time you went to a doctor's office, PT clinic, or some other healthcare provider for an initial appointment, consultation, or "new patient visit." When did you finally get to share your story, experiences, and feelings about your diagnosis, condition, or situation? Odds are that you were able to finally express your concerns or explain your situation only after you had: (1) scheduled an appointment, (2) filled out ten pounds of paperwork which included information about insurance coverage and payment information, (3) sat in at least a (if you're lucky) waiting room, (4) had basic vitals and measurements taken by a medical assistant or other staff member, and then (5) waited, again, for the clinician or provider to see you in an exam room.

What if you were able to share about your situation and circumstances from the very beginning?

Here's a simple framework for on-boarding patients that follows what I call a bottom-up approach when a patient (or prospective patient) calls the clinic:

- Get their narrative experience (ask open-ended questions to get the patient's own perspective, or story, of their situation); get their experiential perspective
  - Tell me a bit about what's going on?
  - How is this affecting your day-to-day life?
  - How do you feel about [insert pain or limitations]?
- Collect the referral info
  - How did you hear about us?
  - What made you reach out to us?
- Understand their goals for treatment
  - What are your goals for treatment?
  - What would you like to be able to do after treatment?

- Understand their expectations about the treatment and the process
  - What do you hope to get out of treatment?
  - How do you see [insert treatment] helping?
- Move onto the administrative information
  - Let's get you scheduled...
  - Demographic information (date of birth (DOB), address, and so on)
  - Payment and insurance information
  - Get e-mail address and provide next steps (online intake paperwork, and so on)
- Answer any questions they may still have
  - Are there any questions you have that I haven't already addressed?
- Assure them they are in good hands, and validate their decision to book an appointment
  - You're in the right place. We're looking forward to helping you address [insert diagnosis or limitation]

Now, look at that flow of the information collected in that preceding process. You not only end up with the necessary information (administrative, demographic, and insurance), but you also get some insight into the patient's situation. On top of that, the order in which you obtained that information was entirely patient-centered. You give the patient the opportunity to share their experiential perspective before you get to the traditional and necessary information. Following this process leaves patients with a unique experience that builds trust, increases their confidence in your clinic's ability to help them, and increases the odds of them showing up to their first appointment.

Summary

At the end of the day, patient engagement and experience don't hinge so much on one or two large events, but rather on the myriad of small touch points they encounter along the way. Everything from marketing, to messaging, to communication, and to front desk operations adds up to either a positive or negative overall experience. It's also important to understand how the peak-end rule affects the patient experience of our clinics and services. At least on the bright side, improving patient engagement and experience doesn't have to be one huge, monumental undertaking. It can be broken down and handled in small chunks. With each touch point addressed, patient experience and engagement improve little by little.

Start with the small processes and procedures, like the sign-in/check-in process. Maybe, adjust a form or two in your intake paperwork. Whatever you do, prioritize making those processes and policies patient-focused, rather than setting them up for clinic or facility convenience.

CHAPTER 4

Commitment #4

Confidently Communicate Value

We will confidently communicate the value that our treatments and services provide to the patients who receive them.

For decades, clinics and clinicians have relied on being "in-network" to avoid having to talk about value. And, in reality, they didn't have to. Patients simply went where their doctors sent them. But, all that has changed. Patients are beginning to be pickier about which provider they seek out.

Rising healthcare costs—deductibles, copays, and coinsurance—combined with the advent of the Internet mean that patients now have a choice in who they see. And, they're beginning to use it. That means we must be able to effectively communicate the value we bring to the table. We must have value discussions with our patients—having them identify their desired goals or outcomes, attaching metrics to those outcomes, and framing the cost of treatment in terms of achieving those goals.

So, what makes patients choose one clinic over another? What makes them choose to receive treatment at all?

I'll answer these questions with a story.

What can a violinist, a subway station, and 1,097 subway travelers teach you about whether patients choose to stay with your clinic, whether they choose a competitor, or whether they choose to opt out of treatment?

Let's take a look ....

On January 12, 2007, a violinist posted up at the L'Enfant Plaza Station in the Metro DC area. It was around 08:00 a.m., so it was a rush hour. For 45 minutes, he played several classical pieces on his violin, as people shuffled through the station, heading to their offices. Almost

1,100 people passed by him that morning. Seven people stopped to listen for over a minute, and 27 stopped to put some money in the open violin case, totaling $32 and some change. That means the other 1,070 people simply walked on by, not seeming to notice the violinist.

Why does this matter?

Because the violinist playing that morning was Joshua Bell, one of the most famous and accomplished musicians at the time [1]. What's even more surprising is that only one person who walked by actually recognized him. Now, this is a performer who makes thousands of dollars a night, playing to sold-out concert halls. Yet, only 27 of the people—just 2.5 percent—who passed by him that day in the subway station noticed, cared, or paid attention.

Let that sink in for a moment ....

One of the world's most famous musicians stops in a public train station and plays some of the most famous classical pieces of music to a crowd of people, and no one really noticed. Why?

The answer lies in contexts and expectations.

Expectations Matter

Whether we realize it or not, our expectations shape our perceptions and experiences of the world around us. In fact, some published research even suggests that our expectations affect what we see (or, at least, what our brains tell us we see) [2]. To illustrate this example, take a look at Figure 4.1.

To read more about this particular image, check out the MIT web page [3].

Figure 4.1 Visual illusion
Source: Edward H. Adelson

This visual illusion plays a "trick" on our brains. We see the original picture (on the left) and notice the shadow cast by the green cylinder. Given what we know about shadows and light, our brains *expect* there to be a difference between the colors of boxes A and B. However, when the gray lines are added (in the image to the right), we notice that they are both, in fact, the same color.

What does this tell us?

It tells us that our expectations impact how we perceive the world around us in a very real way.

Expectations, Perceptions, and the Role of Context

Our expectations also play a role in the placebo effect. Some researchers even refer to these as *expectancy effects*. These effects have been studied by clinical psychologists, neuroscientists, behavioral neuroscientists, and many more. And their research shows that expectancy effects can have a lasting influence and impact on cognitive processing and behavioral actions [4]. Put plainly: we experience the world and make decisions based on those experiences. *What* we experience and *how* we experience it result from our perception of the world around us. Our perception is greatly influenced by our expectations. And, what has a major influence over our expectations? That's right, the *context* in which we find ourselves.

In other words, the environment or context affects our expectations. Our expectations influence our perception. And our perception affects what we experience, how we experience it, and the thoughts, choices, or actions that result from that experience. Figure 4.2 illustrates this idea, showing the foundational role that context and environment play on our individual experience.

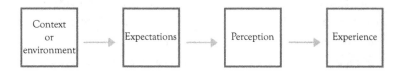

Our environment or context affects our expectations. Our expectations influence our perception. And our perception affects what we experience, how we experience it, and the thoughts, choices, or actions that result from that experience.

Figure 4.2 Context to experience

So, going back to that train station in 2007, is it any wonder most people simply walked on by one of the most famous violinists in the world as he played? In reality, the answer is "no." The people traveling through the station that day didn't *expect* to encounter a world-famous musician playing in the lobby that day. They didn't expect that because they were traveling through a train station on a busy morning before work. Their *context* didn't tell their brains to expect anything out of the ordinary, and therefore, they didn't *perceive* anything out of the ordinary. How many times had they traveled through that station and seen or heard some amateur musician playing the same type of music, with their case open trying to make a few bucks? Probably, countless times. So, when they saw Joshua Bell playing in the same lobby, their brains told them not to expect anything spectacular, that he was probably just another amateur musician trying to pick up a few extra bucks.

This story should make you rethink the context or environment you create in your clinic, and how that may be affecting patient experience, engagement, and satisfaction. As the violinist in the subway station points out, people's expectations impact their experience. You should try to create an environment—a context—that gives your patients the *expectation* that the services you provide are valuable and effective.

The Impact of Expectations on Perceived Value and Satisfaction

As discussed earlier, patient expectations can have a real impact on their experience in a clinic. In fact, clinical research has shown that an initial appointment/consultation can alter a patient's expectations for treatment, resulting in higher (or lower) satisfaction scores [5]. This gives hope that, even if a patient may have low expectations going into an initial visit, they can leave that appointment with high expectations, increased engagement, and even a higher level of satisfaction.

But, how many clinicians understand a patient's expectations? Recent research shows that many clinicians and healthcare organizations don't fully understand a patient's expectations [6, 7]. In fact, many organizations miss important patient expectations such as being given reassurance about treatment, receiving advice about their condition or diagnosis, information about the benefits/limitations of certain treatment options, and opportunities to discuss their problems with their healthcare providers [6, 8]. These expectations may seem like common sense, but many healthcare providers do not address them.

These expectations can also be influenced by the environment of the clinic as well. For example, if a patient goes to check-in for their first appointment and the front desk staff seems hurried, rushed, or dismissive, that patient may expect the same type of experience from the interaction with the clinician. Since expectations influence perception, you'll have to work hard to overcome those low expectations.

Another interesting finding from this research, which ties into context and its effect, is that previous interactions with healthcare providers or experiences in other clinics have a strong influence on patient expectations [6]. How many times have you heard something like this from a patient: "Well, the last clinic I went to …?" Whether it was an amazing experience or a negative one, that experience influenced that patient's expectation for what *your* clinic or clinicians can do for them. Understanding how your patient may feel about your clinic and treatment based on their past experiences in healthcare allows you to address and correct any potentially negative expectations upfront. It also gives you the opportunity to address their expectations, helping you build the case for the value you bring to the table.

How Context Affects Patient Experience, Engagement, and Retention

We've got an understanding of how the context or environment can impact a person's perceptions and experience. Now, let's discuss how you can take that understanding and apply it in your own practice, clinic, or organization. The first thing to take a look at is how your clinic's environment may be affecting patient expectations. From there, you can build, from the ground up, and an intentional environment, culture, and context that molds a patient's expectations toward the positive.

Context Affects Patient Expectations

As stated above, our environment or context influences our expectations. The same is true when your patients walk into your clinic. This fact means

that you need to be aware of what expectations your clinic may be elic-
iting in your patients. Now, when I say that the context or environment
can influence expectations, it's important to note everything that can be
included in "context." Obviously, this includes the physical space itself.
The physical environment, layout, and organization of your clinic impact
not only your patient's expectations but also the overall experience they
have in your facility (read more about that https://rehabupracticesolu-
tions.com/biopsychosocial-patient-experience/).

If your clinic is dirty, cluttered, or disorganized, your patients may
come to expect the same about the services you provide or the skills and
competence of your clinical and administrative staff. I've spoken with
many patients over the years who have said something along the lines
of: "Well, their office is always a mess. It's no wonder they haven't sent
over those records." At the very least, your clinic should be clean, well-
organized, and inviting to patients and prospective patients. Another reason to pay close attention to the physical environment is that expectations
have been shown to influence and alter visual perception [6]. Put plainly:
if your patients expect to see clutter, dirt, or grime, they're actually more
likely to see it in your clinic (even if it's not really there!) (Figure 4.3).

Aside from the physical environment of your clinic, what I would
consider more important is the context of interpersonal interactions. Interpersonal interactions between clinicians and patients play a large role in
patient experience and engagement. And context influences whether an
interaction between the clinician and the patient is positive or negative.
Take something as simple as body language as an example. I'm sure you've
heard of the "point of service documentation" before. It's supposed to be

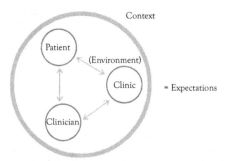

Figure 4.3 Biopsychosocial impact on expectations

great for improving productivity, efficiency, and speeding up the documentation process. But, what are the potential costs of inserting the point of care documentation within the context of a patient–clinician interaction?

When I worked at the VA, I was part of a team that helped roll out an initiative that was rooted in relationship-based care. The aim of the program was to improve both employee (clinician) and patient experience and engagement during the healthcare process. Part of the project included interviews and surveys with patients about things they felt were important for a high-quality healthcare experience. One of the most cited factors by patients we interviewed and surveyed revolved around what clinicians call the point of service documentation. Patients said things like: "At *XYZ* clinic, you know they don't care about you because they have their nose stuck in their computer the whole time they're talking to you." In many cases, inserting this type of documentation into the context of a normal patient–clinician interaction not only impacted that patient's experience of that particular appointment, but it also had a lasting impact on what that patient *expected* from that clinic in the future.

Now, I'm not saying that point of service documentation is evil and you should never do it. But, what I am saying is that you need to be conscious about *when* and *how* you use it during patient evaluations, assessments, and treatments. For example, it's entirely appropriate to be taking ROM measurements of a patient's hand or digits, and be inputting that into the computer as you're taking measurements. I would argue that it's entirely *inappropriate* to be typing up what a patient is saying during an initial interview. During that time, the patient *expects* you to hear, listen, and engage with them and their story. They want you to acknowledge and validate their feelings about their diagnosis, injury, or experience. In situations like that, put the computer away and be present to your patient.

Expectations Affect Patient Perception

The results from a recent survey that I completed on outpatient clinics showed that one of the main reasons clinic owners and managers cited for patients not completing their plan of care was "unrealistic expectations" [9]. In fact, that's a common excuse clinic owners, managers, and directors use to explain why patients stop showing up for therapy.

Now, usually, a patient has unrealistic expectations for a couple of reasons. First, they may have been given unrealistic expectations by the provider that referred them. Other times, it results from miscommunication or lack of communication between your clinic and the patient. Either way, you need to address expectations with patients at the first appointment. You do this by both educating the patient on their condition/diagnosis, the prognosis, and possible treatment options, and by having a value discussion with the patient. You need to explain what the treatment options are, what their anticipated results are, and then how you (or your clinic) fit into that outcome. Addressing expectations early prevents any misunderstandings and also gives you a chance to demonstrate and explain your value.

Again, a patient's expectations affect their perceptions about treatment and results. If they come to you with incorrect expectations, you need to address it early, so that they're more likely to have an accurate and positive perception of the treatment you provide and the outcomes they experience.

Patient Perceptions Affect Patient Experience and Engagement

Now, what happens if a patient's expectations are unrealistic? Let's say they are overly optimistic about the timeline and magnitude of the outcomes they'll experience after a few sessions of treatment in your clinic. They show up for appointment #1, thinking that you'll "do something" to their sore shoulder and it will feel better.

What happens when you do provide some manual therapy to their shoulder and they still have pain afterward (or, it "works" for a bit, then the pain comes back)? Maybe, the patient becomes discouraged. Maybe, they begin to think that "it's not working." Or, they think "why am I even wasting my time/money coming here?"

If you don't take the time, at the beginning to address these expectations and provide a realistic picture of what was going to happen and what to expect, you'll find yourself with patients who become disengaged, unhappy, and unsatisfied. If you do address expectations early, you increase the odds of patients having a positive perception of both the treatment you provide and the experience of their outcomes. They become increasingly engaged and satisfied with the clinic, their clinician, and the services they receive. And that leads to them sticking around to complete their plan of care and maybe even for another round of treatment.

At the end of the day, it's important to realize one thing: context plays a huge role in what your patients experience in your clinic. Context affects a patient's expectations, which impacts their perceptions, and their perceptions impact their overall experience. Just like with the placebo effect, a patient's expectations inform their brains of what they are (or are not) experiencing. *What* we experience and *how* we experience it result from our perception of the world around us.

Think of it like this:

1. The environment or context affects our expectations.
2. Our expectations influence our perception.
3. Our perception affects what we experience, how we experience it, and the thoughts, choices, or actions that result from that experience.

Understanding this allows you to intentionally address each link in the experience chain to make sure that your patients have the best experience possible in your clinic. That will lead to higher levels of engagement and retention. And that leads to better outcomes for your patients, and increased revenue for your clinic or organization.

Talking Value: Addressing the Most Important Questions for Your Patients

Often as clinicians, we forget why our patients are in our therapy clinics to see us. The reality is that they have a problem, and they believe coming to see you is going to help them overcome whatever limitations or pain they are experiencing. Keeping this in mind, as a clinician, you should make a genuine effort to communicate with your patients regarding their limitations, their expectations, and how you are the right person to help them through the services your clinic or organization provides.

Patients often have questions, either because they don't fully understand the complications and factors in their own unique situations, or because they have never been told what is going on. These patients have a need; a need for qualified and competent information. If you can answer these common questions with confidence, empathy, and understanding, you'll build patient trust, improve patient compliance with established plans of care, and drastically improve patient experience in your therapy clinic.

As Bronnie Lennox Thompson, PhD, shared with me on episode 006 of *The Better Outcomes Show* [10], clinicians should look at themselves as knowledge translators, and that's probably the biggest value we provide to our patients: our ability to take all of the scientific and process information we have and make it relevant and understandable to a patient's specific issues and circumstances.

So, let's take a look at the five most common (and critical) questions that a patient may have when they come into your clinic or facility.

1. What's Going on With Me? (Why Am I in Pain?)

Given today's healthcare environment, it is not unusual for a patient to show up to your clinic without any real understanding of their situation or diagnosis. Though the Internet has made knowledge readily accessible, wading through the vast expanse of research evidence, journal articles, and even blog posts proves a challenge, even for your most intelligent or well-versed patients.

On top of that, many doctors find themselves pressed for time and unable to adequately explain to a patient the many physiological, biological, or psychosocial factors that may be at play in their specific situation. They often end up giving the patient resource material, handouts, or links to web pages in an effort to educate these patients on their diagnosis or limitation.

Patients want answers. They want to understand what is causing their pain or limitations and they need someone who not only understands and is knowledgeable about the subject but is able to effectively explain it in a way that is simple, concise, and easy to understand.

As clinicians, we must view our primary role as knowledge translators for our patients and clients. We take the vast, often technical, knowledge that we've garnered over our years of schooling and clinical experience, and can apply that knowledge and expertise to a specific patient's unique situation. Part of that involves explaining or educating that patient on their situation and possible treatment options.

We must, however, do so in a way that is both clear and easy to understand, and empowering for the patient or client.

Be sure that when you communicate with patients, you use words that calm and avoid words that may agitate or pathologize your patients. Your goal should be to effectively explain to your patients the underlying mechanisms of their pain or limitations while empowering them to overcome those limitations or dysfunctions.

2. What Can I to Do to Fix It?

Once you've clearly explained to your patients what is going on, the next logical question they will ask is what they can do to help themselves. It is important when answering this question that you do not fall into the common trap that entangles most: patients do not want to be told what to do. Especially in today's consumer-driven healthcare environment, patients want to explore their treatment options. They want to know what's out there and they want to be able to decide which treatment option makes the most sense for them and their unique circumstances.

Many patients also want to collaborate with their clinician to develop a plan to get them on the road to recovery.

Far too often, clinicians run through a dull and dry list of: "This is what is wrong with you and this is what you need to do/not do." One of the most important factors of effective communication is listening. You should make an honest and intentional effort to listen to your patients, understand their unique circumstances, and then collaboratively establish a plan of care with them.

This becomes even more important if you are not the first clinician this individual has seen for this specific issue. How many clinicians simply told this person: "Here are some exercises. Do these x times per day and don't do xyz."

Taking the time to simply listen to your patients and then working with them to develop a treatment plan that works for them and their unique situation or life circumstances set you and your clinic apart from the crowd. The reality is that most patients do not experience that in any healthcare interaction. They're simply provided information and prescribed a one-size-fits-most treatment option.

This one simple thing, listening, builds trust between you and the patient, establishes rapport, and increases the odds that your patient will fully participate in the treatment program. Simply taking the time to listen can greatly improve the impact and outcomes of your treatment.

3. How Long Is It Going to Take? (Or, How Long Will I Need to Be in Treatment?)

In this world of "I want it now," it is important for clinicians to be able to educate patients on realistic timeframes for recovery and healing. Patients want to know how long it will take for them to feel better. To answer these questions, you need to understand the biological and physiological processes of tissue healing as well as how comorbidities and other factors may affect the healing process. This is where taking a BSP approach comes into play.

Understanding all those unique factors involved in your patients' situation helps you give them a realistic timeline, or a roadmap, for recovery. You want your patients to understand what processes take place during healing and how long those processes generally take.

A clinician who really understands the healing process and factors that may affect it will be able to confidently answer questions about timeframe, comorbidities, and other patient factors and how they will affect the course of treatment. And, while you obviously can't guarantee a timeframe for healing, you should be able to give a reasonable estimation and explain factors that may impact that process.

By effectively answering these questions, you help your patient trust the advice or recommendations you provide them during your treatment sessions.

4. What Can You (the Clinician) Do to Help Me?

They never teach you this in a school, but even as clinicians, it is your job to sell your services to your patients. Now, I don't mean sell as in a sleazy car salesman who tries to talk you into spending $10k on a beat-up clunker. When I say "sell," I mean that you, as a clinical expert, help your patient make an informed decision. Sometimes, that involves helping a patient develop and commit to a plan of care, or a course of treatment, at your facility. Sometimes, it means that you provide education and information to help the patient make an informed decision about their situation and course of action.

The long and short of it: you must find a way to communicate the value you bring to the table, and then allow the patient to decide for themselves whether what you have to offer makes sense for them and their situation.

Today, more than ever, patients are beginning to shop around and look at healthcare services like they do any other good or service. Patients want to know that you are worth the price they will pay to see you. You as a clinician need to be able to show the benefits of the treatment and services you provide.

Here's an example from the PT and OT world: mounting evidence shows the cost-effectiveness of treatment and how the outcomes of treatment are equivalent to similar, more invasive, treatment options such as surgery or injections. Once you educate yourself on the literature and research pertaining to your particular field or specialty, learn how to clearly communicate that to your patients in a way that highlights the benefits (or value) of the treatment you offer them.

Consider communicating this value using emotional language.

Try to think of it this way: you do not provide healthcare services or treatment in your clinic. You provide a single, one-word emotional outcome to your patients.

What is it?

Is it relief (from pain, limitations, etc.)?

Is it freedom (to participate in their chosen activities)?

What emotional impact does your clinic or practice provide your patients?

Find a way to communicate that outcome (that, desired future state, if you will), and you find yourself in a league of your own, with patients and clients who trust and value your expertise and treatment, and who are willing to commit and become active participants throughout their course of care.

5. How Much Is This Going to Cost?

In today's complex healthcare consumer marketplace, patients are becoming more sensitive to costs for healthcare services. Rising premiums, deductibles, and copays leave patients in a position of having to budget, plan for, and even turn down services that may be cost-prohibitive. You should be upfront and honest with your patients not only about costs of therapy, but also about how long you think it will take them to reach their goals or to recover from their injury.

How many visits should they budget for? Remember, your goal should not be to book as many visits as are authorized. Your goal should be to get your patients feeling better and, in a position, to take over for themselves; whether it be with a home exercise program, activity modifications, or adaptation.

As we'll mention in commitment #6, recent regulatory changes in the United States have tried to codify this principle by requiring clinicians to provide "Good Faith Estimates" to private-pay or out-of-network patients. And while you can make the argument that government regulators should (or shouldn't) be involved in requiring estimates, the fact that the government thought it was a big enough issue to impose regulations tells you something. Patients, or constituents, reached out to their legislators about this problem and wanted a solution.

Because this is the truth: your services and treatment do cost something. It either costs your patient time, effort, money, or all three.

Mediocre, or run-of-the-mill, clinics and healthcare organizations use up every authorized visit and rarely provide enough value to justify the expense. Show your patients that you are committed to getting them better, while also being considerate of the financial burden that therapy services may place on them.

One way to do this involves becoming intentional about patient education and information regarding costs. For example, in my practice, ProActive Rehabilitation and Wellness, we fill out a Financial Counseling Form for every patient, regardless of whether we are required to by regulation. This form shows the patient's insurance coverage, available benefits, and then, clearly and simply, the patient's out-of-pocket expense for each visit in their plan of care.

We don't simply run online eligibility verifications. We take it a step forward and show our patients what those benefits actually mean in real dollar and cents quotes. On top of that, we take the extra step of calling those patients 24 to 48 hours before their appointment with us and giving those quotes to them. That way, they walk into their first appointment with a clear understanding of how much they're expected to pay on day 1.

Our patients regularly tell us that they've never had that type of experience in healthcare before. They're used to going to a medical appointment with a rough idea of the costs they can expect. Sometimes, they have to pay more, sometimes less, but it's always a guess. We've made real, tangible efforts to change that paradigm for patients coming to our clinic. And, we see the benefit of this strategy with engaged patients who not only buy into their plan of care but also recommend us to their friends and family.

Real-Life: Addressing Objections and Value Perception

OK, now that we've addressed the value discussion and communication side of the equation, let's look at the most common reasons that a patient may choose to cancel appointments or opt out of care. Here's a spoiler alert: they all have to do with a patient's perception of the value of the treatment or service.

These examples come from the 2019 outpatient owners and managers survey that we completed at Rehab U Practice Solutions and have remained relatively consistent in the subsequent 2020 and 2021 surveys [9]. As I explain later on, most of these objections (because that's really what they are) often have little to do with the reason being cited and are more likely linked to the patient's perception of the value your services do (or would) provide.

Time Commitment and Scheduling Difficulties

So, let's look at the first of the factors: the **Time Commitment and Scheduling Difficulties**. On the surface, this may seem like a legitimate factor, and in some cases, there may actually be scheduling conflicts that prevent a patient from completing their plan of care. However, more often than not, this is a priority problem, not a true scheduling conflict.

Why is it a priority problem, because the patients don't see coming to treatment as more valuable than whatever else they have to do. Patients are busy. They've got jobs, families, and other commitments. If your services aren't seen as truly valuable, there will always be a "scheduling conflict" that keeps patients from showing up.

Unrealistic Expectations

Then there's **Unrealistic Expectations**. Now, we've just discussed how expectations affect perception, so you know this is an important one to address.

Usually, a patient has unrealistic expectations for a couple of reasons. First, they may have been given unrealistic expectations by the provider who referred them. Other times, it results from miscommunication or lack of communication between your clinic and the patient.

Either way, you need to address expectations with patients at the first appointment. You do this by both educating the patient on their condition/diagnosis, the prognosis, and possible treatment options and by having a value discussion with the patient. You need to explain what the treatment options are, what their anticipated results are, and then how you (or your clinic) fit into that outcome.

Addressing expectations early prevents any misunderstandings and also gives you a chance to demonstrate and explain your value.

The Cost of Treatment

And lastly, **the cost of treatment**. Whenever someone brings up price or cost as an objection or reason they can't complete treatment, there's often a deeper reason. Some patients have legitimate financial limitations and can't afford treatment. In those instances, you should work with them to make sure they can still receive as much treatment as possible, given their limited resources.

Most of the time, however, the cost is a smokescreen for something else. Usually, it's value. The patient doesn't value the treatment you provide and therefore is not willing to pay for it. This is related to the priority problem mentioned above.

So, what can you do to help these patients prioritize both the time commitment and the cost of treatment? You need to have a *value discussion* with them. You need to sit down with the patient and have them identify their desired goals or outcomes. Then, you need to attach objective metrics to those goals or outcomes. After that, you frame the cost of treatment as the price to achieve those outcomes or goals.

By having a value discussion with patients, you help them prioritize both coming to and paying for treatment.

Summary

Ultimately, you must understand that your patients' perception matters more than your own. If your patient doesn't expect (therefore perceive) that your services are valuable enough to pay for them (either with time, effort, and ultimately, money), they won't schedule appointments. It doesn't matter if you can empirically show that your services "improve core metrics" and the like.

Knowing this, you must begin to think about how you can address those perceptions, expectations, and potential objections upfront. I've laid out a few common examples in the previous pages, but it would be a good idea to start a list of common objections your patients may give clinicians and office personnel in your facility or organization. Tally them up. Look for patterns. And begin to formulate your responses to them. That way, you're in a position to clearly communicate the value you provide in a way that will actually make a difference to the patients you see.

I will also take a moment here to note that this whole discussion of value simply pertains to patient-facing communication. In reality, value is subjective and varies depending on the audience's perspective or position in the situation. For example, in healthcare specifically, four stakeholders exist as follows: (1) the provider, (2) the patient, (3) the payer, and (4) the policy maker. Each of these individual stakeholders prioritizes different things and has different expectations and incentives in the greater health-care landscape. For example, an initiative that may result in the need for less treatment or visits for a particular patient may excite the payer and/or patient but would be viewed as a "reduction" or cost to the provider (who, in the world of fee-for-service medicine, is incentivized to "maximize" billable time and who essentially gets paid for the number of treatments or services provided). All that is to say: the chapter has dealt with how a clinician can effectively communicate value to a single stake-holder, the patient. We'll talk a bit more about stakeholders and value in commitment #7: moving away from time-based productivity metrics and reimbursement.

CHAPTER 5

Commitment #5

Prioritize Patient Engagement

We will prioritize patient engagement and experience.

What if I told you that there is a common problem that costs many clinics tens or hundreds of thousands of dollars a year, and most of them don't seem to be aware of it?

What would you guess the problem is?

If you guessed a patient dropout or a problem with patient retention, you are right. It seems that many clinics, especially those who may be struggling financially, put a lot of effort into, and focus a lot of attention on, getting in front of referral sources to increase the numbers of patients coming inside their clinic door. They think they have a patient acquisition problem.

But as I'll argue below, they may more than likely have patient retention difficulties.

Now, I will preface this discussion by noting that the examples provided in this chapter do focus on and pertain to a certain subset of healthcare clinicians who treat patients for a specific condition over a series of visits; for example, physical and occupational therapists. While the examples may be specific to this sector of the healthcare industry, the principle applies to many, if not all, subspecialties and areas in healthcare.

For example, pain management clinics, primary care offices, pediatrician practices, and any other healthcare specialties that serve patients and help them manage their overall health for the long term, including the management of chronic conditions, benefit from considering the impact of patient engagement, and retention across the entire course of care. The biggest example I can think of relates to chronic conditions such as diabetes management and similar diagnoses. I was speaking to a friend of mine who works in a nephrology practice as a physician's assistant. I mentioned to him that I was writing this book and wanted to include a section on patient engagement and retention, but was concerned that it may be too narrow of a topic for this type of book. He simply replied with the fact that, in his world of nephrology and chronic kidney disease management, they refer to chronic kidney disease resulting from uncontrolled diabetes as "the disease of noncompliance." This comment opened my eyes to the fact that, though this issue of patient engagement may have a more immediate impact on the financials of a clinic involved in defined courses of care, like PT and OT clinics, it still has a great effect on long-term clinical outcomes across the healthcare industry.

So, that being said, let's look at the financial impact of poor patient engagement retention.

The Big Money Problem

Let's take a look at an example that is close to my heart, that is, patient retention for PT and OT clinics.

Did you know that approximately 14 percent of therapy (PT/OT) patients do not show up for their follow-up appointments? In fact, between 20 and 30 percent will not show up to their third appointment and up to 70 percent of patients will fail to complete their full course of care [1]. That may seem like a staggering number, but it seems pretty consistent with what I've noticed during my time in the outpatient orthopedic rehab world.

That's why many clinics try to prebook (or book out) all the appointments in a patient's plan of care. If they're already on the books, there's a higher chance they'll show up to those appointments; at least, in theory. Even this, though seems to fall short in getting patients to complete their plan of care. (I tend to think this has to do with clinicians not understanding some important factors in behavioral change.)

But, why exactly is this a problem?

Because decreased patient retention costs both patients and clinics … big time.

Financial Cost to Clinics

Let's run some quick numbers on a small/average clinic. This clinic employs five clinicians, each scheduled to see 10 patients per day (50 total patients per day). Now, according to recent industry trends, the average cost for a PT/OT visit is around $100 [2]. The average course of care in the outpatient orthopedic rehab world tends to be 12 visits. That means from a group of 50 patients, the clinic expects to generate around $60,000 (50 patients × 12 visits × $100 average revenue per visit).

Now let's factor in what happens if the clinic experiences the patient drop-off described previously. Let's say that 20 percent of patients don't show up to their third appointment and that another 20 percent drop off every four appointments thereafter. The impact of patient retention on revenue starting with the original 50 would look something like the table shown in Figure 5.1.

As stated earlier, typical revenue expectations for the 50 patients would be **$60,000**.

However, the *actual* revenue after patients dropped out was only **$41,000**. That means this clinic actually experiences a **$19,000** loss for every 50 patients they treat.

So, over three months (12 weeks), this clinic loses $19,000 on these 50 patients. Multiply that by 4 (to get 12 months in a year), and you get around **$76,000**, and that is assuming the clinic only brings in 50 new patients every 12 weeks!

In total, patient dropout can cost average clinics around $150,000 per year (even more, if you're running larger and/or multisite practices!). In a world of constantly decreasing margins and reimbursement reductions, the last thing you need as a clinic owner is to be losing six figures a year.

Visit	Retention rate	Number of patients	Cost per visit	Revenue (patient x cost)
1	100%	50	$100	$5,000
2	100%	50	$100	$5,000
3	80%	40	$100	$4,000
4	80%	40	$100	$4,000
5	80%	40	$100	$4,000
6	80%	40	$100	$4,000
7	60%	30	$100	$3,000
8	60%	30	$100	$3,000
9	60%	30	$100	$3,000
10	60%	30	$100	$3,000
11	30%	15	$100	$1,500
12	30%	15	$100	$1,500
			Total revenue:	$41,000

Figure 5.1 Revenue impact of low patient retention

Costs to Patients

The problem of patient dropout and poor retention also costs patients because they often drop out of treatment before hitting their goals. These patients stop treatment before they're pain-free and are often still experiencing the symptoms or limitations that drove them to seek out treatment in the first place.

So, what's the solution to this problem?

Well, obviously, we want more patients to finish their plan of care. But how, specifically, do we accomplish this?

Research shows that increased patient engagement results in higher rates of treatment compliance and completion. Patient engagement hinges on the patient experience.

Patients who have positive experiences are shown to have higher levels of engagement. So, it's all about delivering impactful patient experiences.

As I'll discuss in a bit, and in subsequent chapters, interpersonal interactions, communication, and patient education, all impact patient engagement and retention throughout the course of care. As I mentioned earlier, this may have a more immediate impact on some allied health providers such as physical therapists, but it has great implications for other healthcare specialties as well.

Let's look again at the example from the beginning of the chapter about patients with chronic kidney disease that results from uncontrolled diabetes. A poor patient experience at an initial evaluation or consultation with a nephrology group may drive a patient experiencing the early stages of kidney disease and dysfunction to simply not show up for their follow-up appointment in 6 months. Maybe, they go another couple of years before reporting to their primary care office with complaints of muscle cramps, vomiting, nausea, fatigue, and other symptoms associated with the loss of kidney function. Now, this patient gets placed on dialysis and experiences a decline in physical health and function.

Who knows? Maybe, this patient could have prevented that outcome by taking some proactive steps to manage their diabetes and improve their kidney function. But, because they had a poor experience and ended up missing their follow-up appointment, they now find themselves in poorer health and requiring more invasive interventions for recovery.

Patient Retention and Plugging the Holes

Now, this problem of patient dropout affects the business side of any healthcare organization. In fact, increasing visits per month, and mainly new patient acquisition and referrals, drives many healthcare clinics and organizations to invest heavily in marketing efforts aimed at increasing the number of patients coming through their doors every month.

And, when it comes to marketing any healthcare business, there's a lot of talk about allowable acquisition costs, conversion rates, and lead generation. And that makes a lot of sense. I mean, you need new patients coming through your door to keep the lights on, right?

But, what about the patients you're already seeing?

These patients have already raised their hands, voted with their wallets, and come in to see you.

Are you really doing the best to not only serve them but also to retain them? Patients who do not complete their plan of care cost both themselves and clinics in terms of time and money. This usually results from a substandard patient experience and lack of engagement. It's a common fact in business that it costs much more to acquire a new customer than it does to retain current ones.

So, as I like to point out to many clients and prospective clients: if your marketing plan is designed to fill your proverbial "bucket" of patients, does it make sense to spend time and money pouring those leads into a bucket with a giant hole in the bottom?

Every clinic, regardless of marketing strategy or lead generation success, would benefit from focusing on improving patient retention through engagement.

Retention Versus Acquisition

Ok. Let's start with the "why" behind focusing on retention. As mentioned earlier, patient dropout causes many clinics to miss out on a lot of potential revenue. It also keeps patients from realizing the full benefit of the treatment they receive; and, in the case of chronic disease management mentioned earlier, it may cause the patient to require more intense healthcare services later as their medical status declines from inadequate management of their chronic condition.

Still, many clinic owners and healthcare administrators fall into the trap of overinvesting in getting *new* patients in the door. This is despite the fact that data suggests it can be 5× more cost-effective to retain existing customers than to acquire new ones [3]. Despite this fact, only about 16 percent of businesses (healthcare organizations included) actually employ a primary marketing strategy aimed at improving patient or customer retention [3].

According to some studies, increasing patient retention by as little as 5 percent can increase profitability by at least 25 percent [4]. Understanding this, it should be clear that knowing how to define, calculate, and improve patient retention would be a worthwhile investment for any clinic owner or manager.

Defining Patient Retention

There are two types of patient retention that every therapy clinic should be aware of and actively track: (1) course of care retention and (2) clinic retention [5].

Course of Care Retention

The course of care retention simply refers to the number of visits a patient attends versus the number of indicated or authorized visits. It is usually calculated as a percentage. This is also referred to as the *Patient Retention Rate (PRR)* calculation.

For example, let's say a patient is evaluated in your clinic, and the evaluating therapist recommends 10 visits to complete the course of treatment. The patient only attends eight visits before discontinuing care (self-discharging) and does not reach their goals. Let's brush off some basic math skills: $8 \div 10 = 0.8$, which is equal to 80 percent.

Now, the best thing about this PRR calculation is that it enables us to see the revenue that is *lost* due directly to patient dropout. So, in our previous example, a PRR equal to 80 percent means this clinic is operating **20 percent below maximum potential revenue.**

What if you were able to improve this clinic's PRR by half? What could that 10 percent do for that clinic's business?

Every clinic should track PRR for each individual patient as well as track the overall clinic PRR. If you are only tracking visits per case, you could potentially be overlooking the underlying reasons that patients self-discharge from your clinic. More on that later.

Clinic Retention

Clinic retention refers to the number of patients who return to your clinic for a new course of care. This can be harder to track, but it is worth it to better understand how to get "return customers" into your clinic. Perhaps, a patient was being treated for shoulder pain and they are now back to be treated for wrist or back pain. Whatever the case, it means that this patient had a good experience at your clinic and your clinic made a positive impression on them.

What is also common about patients who return to your clinics for new courses of treatment? They are often your biggest fans, telling everyone they know about how great you are and how much you helped them. If they were referred to your clinic by a PCP or Specialist, they likely have told that doctor about their experience with your clinic. This can lead to that referral source feeling confident in referring more patients to your clinic. These patients can also influence their friends if/when it comes time for them to seek services.

So, overall, you want to be able to identify these patients and understand *what* caused them to return to your clinic. That way you can replicate that process with as many patients as you can. A simple method to track this could be implementing a patient survey system that gathers data at the time of an initial evaluation and time of discharge.

Increasing Patient Retention

So, now that we know how important patient retention can be for your clinic, how do you go about improving it?

It all starts with the first experience a patient or potential patient has with your clinic. And it continues until you at last discharge that patient from your services. Improving your clinic's patient retention is a continuous process of building trust and relationships with potential, current, and former patients. Some refer to this process as "patient relationship management" or "patient engagement." I like to refer to is simply as "Patient Focus" or a "Bottom-up Approach." It all revolves around the experience your patients have in your clinics.

Patient Experience: Contact Points

Regardless of your area of expertise, patient population demographics, or referral sources, one thing is for certain: the experience your patients have with your clinic will greatly affect not only their retention, but it can even affect their perception of your service delivery. That means if your patient has a lousy experience at their first appointment, they're less likely to complete their course of treatment, and if they do, they will perceive the services you provide as average, mediocre, or even noneffective.

The first step in creating an outstanding patient experience is to first take a look at all the ways that patients and potential patients interact with your clinic. This list should cover everything from what happens when a patient gets referred to your clinic up to the time they are discharged from your services. It takes some time and attention to detail, but what you want to do is get on paper every single point of patient (customer) contact with your clinic.

The next step is to break down each contact point and look for ways to either improve it or differentiate it.

For example, when a patient shows up at your clinic for their first appointment, what happens?

Do they get a stack of paperwork to fill out?

Insurance card, copy of their ID, past medical history, blah blah blah.

I think everyone who has ever been to any healthcare appointment is familiar with that routine.

But, what can your clinic do to improve that process?

Perhaps, e-mailing or mailing the paperwork to your patient ahead of time is an option. That way, your patient can just show up, turn in their packet (or maybe, they've already e-mailed it to you and the therapist has been able to review it), and wait to be seen. Anything you can do to take the pain and drudgery away from that first appointment paperwork packet will help you create a different and outstanding experience for your patients.

Patient Experience: Education and Engagement

When patients show up at your clinic, it can be assured that they will have questions for you. At the minimum, your clinic staff or therapists should be able to answer the five most important questions your patients may have (we'll talk about that more in Chapter 6), but it is also good to provide each new patient with a FAQ sheet (or have one on the website or e-mailed to new patients) that can cover everything from where to park to some basics about your clinic's rehabilitation process.

In addition, it's a good idea to ensure that your patients have some reliable way of getting in contact with you in case they have questions the day after their appointments. This can be telephone, e-mail, and secure messaging. There are a plethora of options out there. I'd suggest looking at selecting one that will improve and differentiate your patients' experience.

Patient education isn't just about getting some facts across to your patients. It's also one of the best ways that you and your clinicians can demonstrate *value* to your patients. The reality is that, often you only have one shot to show your patient the value you bring to the table. If you can't convince them on day one, at that first appointment, that your services are important and can make a difference, the odds are that they will be semicompliant at best, and will not complete their course of treatment at worst.

When communicating with your patients, try to use *emotional* language.

For example, try and think of it like this: you do not provide healthcare treatment or services in your clinic.

You provide a single, one-word emotional outcome to your patients.

What is it?

It could be a relief (from pain, limitations, dysfunctions, etc.). It could be freedom (to participate in their chosen or meaningful activities). What emotional impact does your clinic or practice provide to your patients? Your goal should be to communicate this to every single patient that walks into your clinic in a way that shows them you truly care about them, their situation, and their recovery.

In fact, the way you communicate with your patients directly impacts their overall engagement during their course of treatment. Clinicians who actively listen and communicate with their patients find that their patients are more compliant with recommendations and home programs and generally have a more positive experience throughout the therapeutic process.

Actively listening to your patients' concerns, questions, and difficulties helps you build a trusting relationship with them and also helps you provide services that are *relevant* to each patient's specific situation. Think about how many patients go to their therapy appointments every week, get heat, run through their cookie-cutter treatment program, and then go home. It's no wonder these patients don't feel engaged in the treatment. They probably don't see the need for even showing up anymore.

But, what if their clinician listened to them and their situation, then at their next appointment, that therapist had developed a personalized and tailored treatment plan specifically designed to address the concerns they had expressed? Odds are that the patient would be blown away. They'd *know* that this clinic was different. And, they'd probably tell everyone they know about the great care they received. That's what you want: patients that turn into raving fans; little mini-megaphones that shout your praises. It's in no way easy, but incredibly worth the effort. Going above and beyond to provide real value and an outstanding experience pays dividends in the long run.

The Importance of Patient Engagement and Experience

If all you want to do is run a therapy mill or an assembly line practice, then you don't really care about patient engagement or experience. I mean, you want patients to have a good enough experience that they'll come back for their next treatment, sure. But, you don't necessarily care about their engagement in treatment, and you may not make decisions that incentivize the patient to get the most out of their treatment.

Clinics and clinicians that want to make an impact in their patients' lives think differently. They prioritize patients being actively engaged in treatment. They want patients to be involved in the goal-setting, treatment planning, and benchmarking. This ensures that each patient has a higher chance of achieving their desired goals and outcomes. This is commonly referred to as patient engagement and is connected to patient experience.

Recently published research explores factors that influence patient experience and satisfaction with PT services. Let's take a dive into some of this research and pull out some nuggets that will hopefully help you improve patient experience and engagement in your clinic or facility.

Research on Patient Experience and Satisfaction

Recent events and changes in the healthcare industry, specifically in the United States, have led many organizations to wonder how to measure the quality of healthcare services. For a long time, objective—or standardized—data and outcomes were used to measure "quality" in healthcare. However, over the past few years, researchers started to take a look at more qualitative data, centering around patients' satisfaction and experience with the services they receive. It makes sense if you think about it: how can you rate the quality of service by the numbers alone?

Healthcare should center and focus on the patient. That means that patients should have a say about whether a service is good or bad. Large healthcare companies and universities began researching just that subject.

Research on Patient Experience and Engagement: Main Takeaways

So, what does the research say about patient satisfaction with rehab or therapy services? Well, a systematic review published in 2011 showed that there were two main factors that determined a patient's satisfaction with musculoskeletal outpatient rehab services. These two factors include the interpersonal attributes or skills of the therapist/clinician and the process of care [6].

One interesting finding was that treatment outcomes were infrequently or inconsistently associated with patient satisfaction [6]. Do you know what that means? It means that your patients care less about the outcome of treatment than they do about the *process* involved in receiving care and the *interpersonal* skills of their clinician. If the clinician is personable, makes the patient feel comfortable, and builds a strong, trusting therapeutic relationship with the patient, that clinician will receive a higher satisfaction rating than a clinician who may be technically the better of the two.

What often separates clinicians whose patients leave high satisfaction ratings from those whose patients leave poor ratings has little to do with technical skill or knowledge. It has more to do with the *human connection* that the patient experiences, or doesn't experience, in the clinic.

Now, this isn't to suggest that you can be a mediocre clinician and hope to succeed in the long run. This is healthcare, after all, and there is an expectation that patients will benefit from treatment or services. All the interpersonal skills in the world won't help you out if your patients feel the treatment they receive is subpar. But, this research does suggest that, given two clinicians that are at least competent in their field, the clinician with better interpersonal skills and a great process in place will tend to have higher patient satisfaction ratings.

Interesting Findings From the Research

A systematic review published in 2011 divided quantitative data about patient satisfaction and engagement into three subgroups: degree of patient satisfaction, patient characteristics, and aspects of treatment associated with satisfaction [6]. One interesting finding about the degree of patient satisfaction was that, on average, patients generally reported satisfaction with outpatient therapy between 68 and 91 percent of the time [6]. Now, these findings include patients and clinics across Europe, so there may be some variation in other areas such as the United States, Canada, and other parts of the world.

Another interesting finding revolves around the status or level of injury. According to this research, patients tend to report higher satisfaction with outpatient therapy services if they are seen or treated for acute musculoskeletal conditions rather than those experiencing chronic pain [6]. This means that those of us treating patients in chronic pain need to step up our own game, both in the process of care delivery as well as in our own interpersonal skills and interactions.

In fact, research shows that patients experiencing chronic pain place greater importance on the *process or organization* of care. Those patients experiencing acute injuries or conditions placed greater weight on the clinician's interpersonal skills [6].

Understanding the results of this research helps us organize and structure our clinics to better meet the needs and expectations of patients depending on where they are in their recovery process and what they consider most important.

Process and Organization of Care

Let's take a look at how the process or organization of care impacts patient satisfaction according to the research. The research outlines factors involved in the process of care as timeliness of treatment, efficiency of treatment, frequency, follow-up, individualized programming, and patient involvement in decision making [6].

For example, patients with chronic LBP considered individualized treatment planning and the ability to contribute to treatment decisions of great importance. This research gives us a road map to an outstanding patient experience. By ensuring that our patients receive timely and efficient treatment that is individualized, with their own input, we can leave patients feeling satisfied, engaged, and truly cared for.

Organization of care also plays a role in overall patient satisfaction with treatment. For example, access to services, convenient clinic hours, location, parking, and approachable and available staff all impact patient satisfaction scores [6]. It should seem pretty obvious, but poor levels of cleanliness or clutter also negatively impact a patient's reported level of satisfaction following treatment.

Treatment Outcomes and Expectations

Contrary to what many may think, clinical outcomes do not always correlate with patient-reported satisfaction levels. For example, according to some published research on the subject, high satisfaction was sometimes—but not always—related to pain reduction [6]. This may be due to the fact that some patients felt that the self-management strategies they learned while in treatment were more important than the reduction in pain. If they were able to manage the pain themselves, they still considered that a "win" so-to-speak.

Also, improving a patient's strength and mobility can have a great impact on their quality of life, even if there is only minimal improvement in symptoms such as pain. This should give us hope that we can still have a positive impact on patients, even if they end up needing to go through with surgery after treatment, or if they are still experiencing pain or some limitations. Especially if we are implementing a BSP treatment strategy, we may be able to positively affect a patient's quality of life—leading to higher treatment satisfaction—even if the underlying symptoms are minimally changed. This means that even patients experiencing chronic pain can experience improvements and feel satisfied with the treatment they receive in our clinics.

Part of what we can do as clinicians to improve a patient's satisfaction and engagement with our services is to help frame or manage expectations at the beginning. Research shows that a patient's expectations of the therapy encounter influence their evaluation of—and satisfaction with—the care they receive [6]. For example, patients with acute conditions tend to have lower expectations and higher satisfaction rates than those experiencing chronic conditions.

Knowing this, we as clinicians would do well to begin managing a patient's expectations at the outset of treatment. This may include providing additional education about the treatment program, recovery rates, what to expect, and so on. If a patient knows what to expect going into treatment, they'll be less likely to be surprised at the end (who knows, maybe they'll even be pleasantly surprised by the gains they weren't expecting!).

Human Connection and the Role of the Clinician

Another interesting finding from the research is that patients reported higher levels of satisfaction when they were treated by the same clinician over the course of treatment [6]. This follows some of the research around patient–therapist interactions, which we'll look at in detail below. It also seems pretty intuitive.

Ultimately, all of healthcare is about one thing: humans helping humans. It is a personal service involving a human experience. Patients want that experience. They want to feel that their clinician understands their situation, knows how to help, and truly cares about them. Consistency helps foster this relationship. It's hard for patients to feel that human connection when they are treated like numbers on a schedule, being seen by whatever clinician is available at that time.

The best clinicians—those that are sought out by patients—are those who are able to make that human connection felt. Let's take a look at how the patient-therapist interaction can affect patient satisfaction and engagement.

Patient–Clinician Interactions

It goes without saying that—at the very least—patients expect to be treated by clinicians who are professional, competent, friendly, and caring. Research also shows that patients place a great deal of weight on the clinician's ability to communicate effectively; from explaining a diagnosis to educating the patient on self-management strategies [6].

In fact, this research concludes that high-quality patient–therapist interactions are more important to patients than convenient clinic locations, parking, organization of care, and even in some cases the treatment outcomes [6]. Given that information, we clinicians and clinic owners should be trying to do anything we can to improve the interactions patients have with our staff and clinicians.

So, how do we improve patient–therapist interactions? Well, the research highlights a few areas that include: (1) a clinician's interpersonal and communication skills, (2) a clinician's practical or technical skills, and (3) individualized treatment planning and organization of care [7]. We've spent a good deal of time discussing that last point above, so we'll focus on the clinician's skills.

Interpersonal and Communication Skills of the Clinician

Research shows that a clinician's active listening, empathy, friendliness, encouragement, confidence, and nonverbal communication all impact a patient's satisfaction and engagement with treatment [7]. These skills play a huge role, not only in developing trust or rapport with patients, but they also impact the organization of care. Take active listening as an example.

When a clinician takes the time to actively listen to and understand a patient's unique situation, it does two things: (1) it allows a bond to develop between clinician and patient, leaving the patient feeling valued and truly cared for, and (2) it helps inform the therapist and gives them the information necessary to tailor the treatment plan to be individualized for that patient.

Think about it: patients want to have their stories heard. They want their therapist or clinician to *understand* where they are coming from, what they've experienced, and how they feel about it.

When a clinician takes the time to actively listen to the patient's story, show empathy, provide encouragement that things will get better, and then confidently explains to the patient the treatment approach, that patient walks away from that encounter thinking: "Wow! That therapist *understands* me and what I'm going through and they *actually* care about helping me get better." Those moments create those experiences that truly leave a positive impact on our patients' lives.

Practical and Technical Skills

Practical and technical skills of the clinician also impact patient [7]. Tying in with the previous example of communication skills, patients tend to feel that a clinician that is able to provide simple and clear explanations has stronger skills or training. That makes sense if you think about it. People who truly understand a subject (or diagnosis) are able to provide simple, clear education or explanations.

On top of being able to explain things clearly, patients also believe it is vital that their clinician possess excellent technical skills and abilities [7]. Whether this involves manual therapy techniques, application of modalities, or exercise prescription, clinicians must show their patients that they have mastered those skills. This is likely due to the fact that patients simply tend to put more trust in clinicians who they feel are expert practitioners.

This reason alone should make all of us who work as clinicians strive for constant improvement and development. After all, the whole reason patients come to our clinics is to receive the expert care we are able to provide. It doesn't matter how efficient the care is delivered or organized, or how the parking is at your clinic. If you are simply adequate as a clinician, you will struggle to deliver an amazing patient experience.

Summing Up the Research on Patient Experience

As we've discussed throughout this chapter, many factors influence patient experiences in our clinics or organizations. Recently published research indicates that the process of care and the interpersonal attributes of the clinician play the biggest role in determining a patient's satisfaction with rehabilitation/therapy care. Ultimately, patients want to experience a *human* connection during their course of treatment.

I hear this all the time when surveying patients at client organizations and in my own clinic. Patients want to feel heard, listened to, and valued. In fact, I encourage all of my client organizations to implement some sort of system to track and measure how well they're making patients feel heard and listened to. One good tool is the CARE Patient Feedback Measure [8].

The practical skills of the clinician do play a role in the overall satisfaction patients report. However, what is arguably just as important is how that clinic, clinician, or organization makes that patient *feel*.

Do our clinics run patients through a mill? Do we make patients feel like numbers on an assembly line, offering cookie-cutter treatment programming? Or, do we strive to learn each patient's unique story—where they are on their road to recovery—to understand how their particular limitation impacts their daily life? The clinics and clinicians that are able to do that will deliver an experience unlike any other in today's healthcare landscape.

Their patients will feel cared for. Their clinicians will feel the pride, impact, and fulfillment of doing truly meaningful work. And, they will rise above the throng of mediocre clinics offering one-size-fits-most treatment programming.

CHAPTER 6

Commitment #6

Embrace Transparency

We will embrace transparency throughout the entire treatment process,
including the financial costs for our patients.

When it comes to transparency, I consider this to include two main areas:
(1) transparency in the process or treatment and (2) transparency in the
financial costs or the expenses of receiving treatment or care.

These play a huge role in patient engagement throughout the treatment process, their experience and satisfaction with the treatment, and
even clinical outcomes. While books have been written about each of
these subjects, I'll try to deliver an overview of each and specifically discuss how each of these two forms of transparency affects the human side
of healthcare, that is, the relationship, confidence, and trust (or lack
thereof), which form out of the way clinics and clinicians handle transparency throughout the healthcare process.

Transparency Throughout Treatment

Now, as a general rule, most patients feel lost when traversing healthcare.
There're a lot of big words, acronyms, and jargon that are obscure and
confusing unless you live it every day. When we talk about transparency
and accessible language, most of the clinicians, academics, and healthcare administrators I speak to tend to think of patients who may not
have the same educational level as healthcare professionals. And, while it
is true that educational attainment may affect a person's understanding
of the healthcare process, having an advanced degree doesn't provide any
extra insight into healthcare's cryptic language.

I've treated lawyers, accountants, and engineers who would run me out of the room in a challenge of intellect and intelligence. Yet, even they had questions arising from a lack of knowledge about healthcare specifically. So, this isn't an issue to be viewed as an initiative of access and inclusion for the uneducated or illiterate. Most patients, unless they work in healthcare, benefit from intentionally clear and simple communication throughout the treatment process. How we educate patients and answer their questions has a big impact on their engagement, their trust and confidence in the treatment itself, and, ultimately, clinical outcomes and satisfaction with the treatment.

Transparency Through Communication: Answering Patient Questions

Let's start with the most common form of communication in healthcare: answering questions. Answering questions is part of every clinician's job and day-to-day routine, whether it's in the original job description or not. From providing basic patient education to instruction in home exercises or standard procedures in the clinic, clinicians often find themselves answering a wide variety of questions.

Questions such as "What's going on with me?," "What does that mean?," and "How many times do I have to come here?" are some of the most common that are asked during an initial assessment or consultation. (Those are the five important questions we covered in Commitment #4.)

How you as the clinician respond to these initial inquiries sets the tone for the entire course of treatment and, as we will discuss later, can have a lasting impact on the clinical outcomes of treatment by affecting a patient's expectations [1]. Your answers can even affect a patient or client's perception of the quality of the care they receive at your clinic or facility. By building a rapport, trust, and clinician–patient agreement, you potentially increase the rates of patient or client compliance, which can have a direct impact on the patient's health, well-being, and outcomes [2].

It's safe to say that any clinician who interacts with patients or clients on a regular basis should understand the importance of that responsibility and how to effectively communicate his/her answers in a way that increases the likelihood of positive outcomes.

Clinical Implications of How Clinicians Answer Questions

As mentioned earlier, clinician–patient communications not only have a direct effect on clinical outcomes and health, but they also have an indirect effect. Every opportunity to communicate with a patient or client provides a chance to build trust, establish rapport, and improve the therapeutic alliance between the clinician and the patient or client [2].

However, that only happens if these instances of communication are handled appropriately. The same way your communication can improve clinical outcomes, it also has the potential to *harm* outcomes or *lessen* the impact of the care you provide to that patient.

To illustrate this point, let's consider the potential impact of how a clinician answers the question, *"Why does my back hurt?"*

This seems like a simple enough question to answer: simply, give the patient or client a rundown on the basic anatomy of the back, common problems or dysfunctions that occur, and then wrap it all up with a likely prognosis and recommendations for how the treatment should go, what exercises or stretches to do at home, and what activities to avoid.

Anyone from a new grad to an experienced clinician could knock that one out of the park, right?

The Impact of Our Words as Clinicians

Though answering the aforementioned question seems to be straightforward and simple, *how* it is answered and the words the clinician chooses to use have a long-lasting impact on that patient. Those words can cause the patient to believe that their back is vulnerable, their injury is serious, or that their outcomes will likely be poor. This leads to the patient having misguided beliefs about their back, their injury, and their prognosis [3].

As I've often written and said in talks, clinicians have more influence on a patient's beliefs and perceptions about pain or dysfunction than almost any other source of information. Saying something that may cause the patient to begin avoiding activities because of fear of pain or injury could result in negative clinical outcomes during and after treatment [4]. Again, this illustrates how the words we as clinicians use have a real impact on not only our patients' perceptions but also their real clinical outcomes.

Aside from the clinical impact our words have on patient outcomes, there are also *nonclinical* implications clinicians must consider. How we communicate with patients can also affect the business side of our practices.

Why Answering Questions Is Important for Business

Whether we'd like to admit it, healthcare—at least in the United States—is a business. We can save the debate on whether this is a good thing for another time. However, the reality is that healthcare services are treated as a commodity. This means that our potential patients or clients are "shopping" around for healthcare services.

Even in the UK, where there is a national single-payer healthcare system, the introduction of "pro-market competition" policies resulted in patients making changes in the hospital or clinic they chose to use [5]. Potential patients were required to be provided with information about five potential hospitals including clinical outcomes and patient satisfaction prior to undergoing treatment. The results showed that "the share of patients bypassing their nearest hospital increased for better hospitals while it clearly decreased for worse hospitals" [5]. Taking cost and price out of the picture doesn't seem to change people's drive to find the highest perceived quality and value for the healthcare services they obtain.

That means clinicians and organizations need to be intentional about how they plan to answer the main question a prospective patient will ask: "Why should I choose your clinic or facility over the one down the road?"

The Internet Changes Things

Now, with the informational revolution of the Internet, patients have access to clinic and provider reviews, websites of potential clinics, and information about what to expect when it comes to cost, quality, and duration of treatment. Prospective patients make judgments about the perceived quality of services offered by a clinic or provider based on what they find on the Internet.

This can be great news if you are in a position to communicate with these "customers" in a way that brings them into your clinic doors. It also means that there are countless clinics and centers trying to advertise to every potential healthcare consumer out there. In the vast sea of providers, clinics, and independent clinicians vying for attention from potential patients—or "customers"—knowing how to stand out from the crowd becomes necessary not only to survive but also to grow your business.

We need to be able to communicate with our patients and potential patients in such a way as not to become lumped into "commoditized" health services that are judged solely on price. How we communicate to prospective patients needs to highlight the value and quality of the services we provide. Part of that can involve positive reviews. But, we want to make the effort to showcase clinical expertise and skill. Just like that example from the UK, prospective patients will drive a long distance to be seen by a clinician they feel will be able to help them address their issue or dysfunction.

Creating Distinction in the Market Through Communication

So, how can clinics, practices, or individual clinicians use communication to make themselves or their clinics look better or more attractive to potential patients than their competitors?

The answer lies in value, or more accurately *perceived higher value*. You may be a physical therapist offering services down the street from another PT clinic. What will drive potential patients to choose you over the competition down the road is whether those patients perceive your clinic or practice as a higher (or better) value.

The way you communicate with patients and potential patients creates a point of differentiation between you and your competition. You must ensure that every point of communication with your patients and potential patients is not only distinct from your competition but also reinforces the higher value you bring to the table.

To quote Scott McKain on the subject: "Unless you become vibrant and committed to making your efforts distinct, your customers will move on" [6].

Now, admittedly there is more to a creating distinction in the marketplace than simply communicating with your patients and potential patients. If that communication is not backed up by *actual* value above and beyond your competition, then you'll still end up struggling. But, let's focus on how to use communication to create distinction for your clinic or facility.

What Do Patients Really Care About?

In order to understand the best way to communicate with patients, we need to first understand how our patients think, what they care about, and what they want to know. Unfortunately, there tends to be a disconnect between what *clinicians* believe to be most important in providing quality care and what *patients* believe to be most important.

Patients typically *"want safe, effective, timely clinical care from skilled clinicians who are able to make them feel personally cared for, included in decision-making and comfortable"* [7].

The reality is that they are making themselves vulnerable to—in most cases—a stranger (that's you) to get some kind of relief, treatment, or care for some condition or dysfunction that is impacting their day-to-day life. As clinicians, we often forget this fact.

We talk a lot about the medical terms, focusing on anatomy, physiology, and prognosis but leave out the emotional dimension of patient care. This emotional component is the strongest driver of a patient's overall satisfaction with a clinic or clinician [7]. This is clearly demonstrated by the fact that roughly just 8 percent of patients consider being provided with literature, diagrams, models, or resource websites to be indicative of quality care [8].

So, what does that mean for clinicians? It means this: while it is certainly important to provide this informational material to patients, clinicians must first and foremost remember that we are treating individuals with unique social and psychosocial needs. Being able to convey that understanding in every aspect of patient communication sets exceptional clinics and professionals apart from the average.

Again, healthcare is a human experience, based on interpersonal interactions, and relationships. That means our patients don't necessarily care about diagrams, models, or resource websites. They want to know how their diagnosis or situation will likely affect their day-to-day life (What does it mean for them?). They also want to know what the options are, and how you, their trusted clinician (or, as I like to say: "healthcare guide"), will help them on their journey toward recovery.

This points back to those questions we asked in Commitment #4. Those questions address what patients really care about. Learn to answer those questions effectively, and you're well on your way to creating that distinction I mentioned earlier.

The Important Questions

Understanding the difference between what patients deem as important factors in the healthcare experience and what clinicians deem as important helps us in answering the most important questions that patients have. We have already covered the five questions every clinician and clinic should be able to answer. Though on the surface these questions may seem simple and straightforward, they provide exceptional (dare I say *distinctive*) organizations and clinicians an opportunity to not only demonstrate their clinical skills and expertise but also provide that emotional connection that patients truly desire in the healthcare experience.

For example, a question about *what* is going on with their particular diagnosis or condition, on the surface, appears adequately answered by a rundown of their diagnosis, prognosis, and recommendations. Clinicians that take it to the next level will weave in patient-specific information and empathy, and communicate it in a way that demonstrates they truly care about that patient and their specific circumstances.

A question about cost could be answered simply by stating the clinic's given prices or pricing scale. Again, clinicians who stand out take the time to not only provide rote information about the pricing of their services but also take the time to (1) acknowledge the financial impact of receiving services, (2) show consideration for the patient's time and resources, and (3) ensure that the patient understands that the clinician's goal is to get them to a position where they are able to take over the recovery process themselves as quickly as possible—*not* to simply book as many visits as insurance has approved. *How* we as clinicians answer questions has more impact on a patient's experience than *what* the answer is. In many situations, the answer may not change from clinic to clinic. A patient with a rotator cuff injury will not receive drastically different clinical information in any therapy clinic, but how that information is communicated can make a huge impact on his/her overall satisfaction with care and perception of the value and quality of a clinic's services.

How to Effectively Answer Questions

Let's wrap up with a few simple strategies for effectively answering questions that our patients or clients may ask. As a clinician, you obviously have a firm understanding of any clinical, anatomical, or physiological components of questions being asked. What we need to remember is that effective communication involves not only understanding our side of it (the answer) but also taking the time to *listen* to our patients before going into our preprogrammed answer for the "XYZ" diagnosis. Especially during an initial assessment, listening during the patient interview process is essential to establishing a strong therapeutic alliance with the patient which can greatly improve both clinical outcomes and patient satisfaction [9].

As mentioned earlier, *how* we answer our patients' questions is much more important when it comes to patient satisfaction and perception of quality than the information we provide (assuming you are providing accurate information—this doesn't count if you are flat out wrong about the clinical aspect of your answer). Because, at the end of the day, any qualified clinician can tell your patient *what* is going on, the prognosis, and recommendations. What we need to focus on is the *value* we bring to the table as clinicians. This means highlighting not only our clinical expertise but also showing our patients that we care about them as individuals. We want them to know that we care about their unique circumstances, comorbidities, psychosocial factors, and ultimately human situations. Because the truth is that's why we got into patient care in the first place: to make real human connections and to make a lasting impact on our patients' lives. And how we answer questions is the first opportunity we as clinicians have to make that connection and impact.

Summarizing Transparency Through the Process of Treatment

It's very easy as clinicians to fall into a mindset of simply leaning on our clinical knowledge and expertise when communicating with patients and clients. We rattle off statistics, prognoses, and recommendations like we're taking a test. It's also easy to take for granted the impact that our words have on our patients—both on their clinical outcomes as well as their psychosocial and cognitive perceptions of their conditions or situations.

You must understand that how you communicate with patients and potential patients has a direct impact on the business side of your clinical practice. In the age of the Internet, you should understand that your patients can uncover all kinds of information and reviews of your clinic or services. And they'll use that information to make decisions about whether to book an appointment with you.

The way you communicate with patients, both in-person at your clinic or online via your website and blog, has a direct impact on how your patients or potential patients judge the overall quality of your services or treatment. You should take the time to consider what patients deem most important to a great healthcare experience and then weave that into every opportunity to communicate with them. At the end of the day, *how* we as clinicians communicate with patients and potential patients has a real and lasting impact on their perceptions of our services and the quality of care we provide.

Transparency of Costs

You know what sucks?

When you call a clinic to set up an appointment for an evaluation or treatment that your doctor prescribed and you can't get answers.

Answer to the questions: "How much is this going to cost me?," "What will my bill be at the end of treatment?" and the like.

Most of the time, clinics respond with something like, "With your insurance, your copay is $X." And that's not untrue. That is the copay. But everyone knows it: about three months after that appointment, you're going to get a bill, and hopefully, it's small. Sometimes, it's a "what the hell is this!?!?" bill.

Either way, this has to stop. We need to do everything we can to be transparent with the patient about what their financial commitments will be. This may be an estimate, range, or we may even go so far as calling their insurance to get hard numbers. What is important is that we begin to pull back the curtain for our patients, to provide them with as much information as possible upfront, so they don't get an ugly surprise afterward.

Confusion in Healthcare Pricing Information

Most patients do not fully understand their insurance benefits or terms like "coinsurance." In fact, some research shows that only 11 percent of healthcare consumers are able to fill out a simple fill-in-the-blank question about the cost of hospitalization [10].

We see this every day in the clinic. We often field questions like, "My card says I have a $25 copay, but it also says I have a 20 percent coinsurance and I know I have a $2500 deductible. How much am I *actually* going to have to pay?"

All of this confusion about healthcare costs and pricing poses serious challenges to patient decision making. This causes patients to make suboptimal, or even poor, decisions simply out of exasperation. In fact, research shows that, when we are confronted with a stressful and confusing decision, we often rely on simple heuristics to make that decision [11]. This often involves something like selecting the first option on the list. Obviously, that's not an effective (or even safe) way to make healthcare decisions.

And the unfortunate reality is that most patients have questions about costs. It can be extremely difficult, even for healthcare providers, to determine a patient's out-of-pocket costs. Part of our vision for healthcare at ProActive is that healthcare providers should act as healthcare guides, and that includes educating patients about treatment options and costs. So, we spend a good bit of time providing explanations and education to patients about their coverage and what that actually means for their costs for treatment.

In fact, we have a policy at our clinic to help overcome some of the confusion. We always check a patient's eligibility and benefits through either the insurance provider's web portal or a clearinghouse portal like Availity. However, as I'm sure you're aware, many times, that information is inaccurate or not up-to-date. So, once we've verified their coverage online, one of our team members either chats online, in real time, with an agent from that insurance company, or calls the insurance provider and gets real-time eligibility and estimate for that patient. This helps us provide the most accurate information possible to patients ahead of their appointments. And most patients are truly grateful for this. In fact, many tell their friends and neighbors about us just because of this process. And that simply speaks to this major problem in healthcare about pricing transparency and cost.

The Need for Pricing Transparency in Healthcare

As consumers, most of us expect that we'll have the opportunity to review the cost of any given item or service before swiping the credit card or handing over any cash. Would you put something in the cart at the grocery store if the tag read "Price applied in 45–60 days" [10]?

Of course, not!

In fact, you'd probably find someone who works at the store to give you a real price. Yet, that is exactly the case in healthcare. Patients, or consumers, have difficulty in finding the actual or real costs (or prices) for any healthcare services. This likely results from the fact that most physician or clinic fee schedules (what they "charge" for services) are not the *actual* cost that is paid for the listed procedures or services.

Why is that the case?

Because most insurance companies negotiate "allowable costs" or "allowable rates" with providers. These rates can be discounted between 40 and 60 percent off of the "listed" fee [10]. These fee schedules can also be discounted heavily for private-pay or self-pay patients.

Here's a great example: my wife and I have, at the time of this writing, five children. We had health insurance for the first two pregnancies. And it was *good* health insurance. Maternity was covered at 100 percent for each delivery. When it was all said and done, we paid around $100 to $200 for some random lab work or tests for each delivery. Talk about a great deal!

Now, when we were pregnant with our third child, I had left the Department of Veterans Affairs and was self-employed as an independent healthcare consultant. For the healthcare coverage, my wife and I decided on a Health Share Organization. These organizations don't act like insurance, but they pool membership fees to cover the healthcare costs of the members. This made us, essentially, "self-pay patients."

So, my wife and I go to our first prenatal appointment. The billing manager at the office says, "Oh, you're self-pay. Here's our fee schedule." I was shocked! At the top was a large number—like $10,000 for the Obstetrician (OB) delivery services. And then, under the large number at the top, was the "self-pay discount." It was $2500. One fee, 75 percent off of the listed fee schedule. It was the same at the hospital: $17,000 on the fee schedule, with a "self-pay" rate of $3500. With discounts and inflated fee schedules like that, it's easy to see why it can be so difficult to find the cost of care.

And being self-pay actually makes it easier. The provider shows you the fee schedule and then allows you to pay the "self-pay" rate at a discount, and you're done. No more bills or costs are expected.

If you have health insurance coverage, it can be much more confusing—coinsurance, copays, deductibles, and out-of-pocket maximums. All of these terms lead to confusion and obscurity when it comes to the actual cost that a patient pays. On top of that, insurance plan networks and approved providers add another layer of complexity.

Is this hospital "in-network"? Does this provider take my insurance? What happens if the hospital is in-network, but the specific provider of the physician group isn't?

And good luck trying to get the answers to specific questions from the insurance provider. When we have called insurance plans on behalf of patients to inquire about benefits, there have been instances where it takes two or three representatives from the insurance plan to check and verify the information they present to us.

This confusion often results in surprise medical bills, often that arrive months after the original episode of care.

Now, this problem garnered enough public outrage that the federal government got involved at the end of 2021.

Recent federal legislation that took effect at the beginning of 2022 aims to remedy this situation. The Consolidated Appropriations Act of 2021, also known as the "No Surprises Act," provided billing protections against surprise medical bills when receiving care from out-of-network providers at in-network facilities [12]. Now, while this legislation does provide protections against bills exceeding $400 of a Good Faith Estimate, it only applies to patients or clinicians who are out-of-network or private-pay. It makes no mention of patients with insurance receiving care from in-network providers and the like.

Without getting into the weeds, or the philosophical arguments for or against these types of regulations, we need to understand that they don't simply form in a vacuum. There was enough public outcry over balance billing and "surprise" medical bills that the federal government decided to step in.

Patients, or consumers, are tired of not knowing how much money they'll have to pay to receive treatment. And, if you remember those five critical questions from Commitment #4, patients naturally want to know how much treatment will cost them.

Now, obviously, the cost is not the only factor when considering the value of healthcare service. As we discussed in previous chapters, value is subjective and is affected by a person's context and expectations. Sometimes, we may choose to pay more because we feel that option is a better value despite the higher cost. Still, cost plays a major role in the purchase decisions of *any* service. And it's our responsibility, as healthcare providers, to make that information as accessible as possible, so our patients can make those value judgments for themselves.

Patient-Centered Healthcare and the Importance of Transparency

When you hear the words "patient-centered care," I'm sure you think of the term in the traditional sense. Growing practice and policy movements continue to push healthcare providers toward patient-centered models of care, which involve the incorporation of a patient's goals and preferences into the medical decision-making process [13].

We learn about it in our schooling. Continuing education courses highlight its importance. Even public service campaigns push us to be more "patient-centered" in our treatment planning and implementation.

However, this is easier said than done in real, day-to-day clinical practice. Much of the difficulty in providing truly patient-centered care stems from a general lack of transparency in the decision-making process.

Oftentimes, patients receive either too little information or too little clinician input to confidently make decisions about their care [14]. This may result from the time constraints placed on clinicians during their clinical days. Productivity standards and utilization requirements often leave clinicians with very little time to adequately provide that key component of decision making: their clinical expertise or input. Often, clinicians find themselves giving a patient a few handouts or a link to a resource page and then asking, "So, what do you think you want to try?"

And that's just on the clinical side of things. As we mentioned in the previous section, this problem is compounded by the lack of cost transparency throughout this process as well. As I mentioned at the beginning of this chapter, there are two parts to transparency in healthcare: transparency about the process of care or treatment and transparency about the costs or financial implications of receiving care.

In order to truly offer "patient-centered" healthcare services, you must find a way to integrate those people-first principles into every facet of care. Whether it be patient intake and onboarding (like that first call framework), communication and answering questions (like in previous chapters), or discussing financial costs responsibilities, you need to put the patient at the center of the process. Patients aren't an afterthought. They're the whole reason that thought exists in the first place.

And the good news is that it often doesn't take an exorbitant amount of time, energy, or resources to make the necessary changes to make the entire process of care truly patient-centered. Several examples and strategies shared thus far in this book can help you approach patient care in a way that makes the patient, the end user or recipient of services, the focus of the entire process.

CHAPTER 7

Commitment #7

Forget Time-Based Productivity

We will forget time-based productivity metrics and find alternative ways to measure our effectiveness as clinicians and receive reimbursement for the care we deliver.

Whether you're a new grad or a seasoned clinician, you've run into the productivity paradigm; using time-based productivity as a way to evaluate a clinician's performance. In reality, these metrics really serve to "maximize revenue" or "improve efficiency" in the clinic or organization.

Now, there's nothing wrong with maximizing revenue or improving efficiency. In fact, I believe you should strive to do both in your organization. Maximizing revenue ensures that your organization has the financial stability to continue serving the local community while improving efficiency enables your organization to serve more patients in a more cost-effective manner.

The problem comes from an almost incessant or obsessive reliance on productivity metrics as a means to optimize revenue and treatment efficiency.

These days, healthcare organizations, hospitals, practices, and clinics run on productivity. They focus on productivity. They *need* productivity. Because, in reality, they're not sure how else to achieve their goals. Especially in an industry dominated by a fee-for-service standard, time-based productivity metrics are a logical choice.

However, by focusing almost solely on time-based productivity measures, we miss what we truly should be assessing. We miss out on measuring the *quality* of the healthcare service being provided. This time-based productivity system creates an incentive structure that causes clinicians to try to "get the most out" of every patient interaction (in terms of bill-able units), which cuts down on documentation and administrative time. However, what is often lost in this environment is the ability to focus on individual patient needs.

It's time we all decided to begin focusing on what really matters: patient-driven outcomes, rather than treatment units and numbers of minutes billed. These patient-driven metrics should be used as a part of every clinic's quality improvement initiatives and can help clinics deliver a level of care unmatched by local competitors.

For example, some validated measures like the CARE Questionnaire provide insight into the person-centeredness of a clinic or organization's healthcare service delivery [1]. It's a simple, 10-question survey that assesses how a clinic or clinician made a patient feel at ease, listened to or understood, and cared for. This, combined with standardized functional measures like the patient-specific functional scale (PSFS), helps clinics and practitioners return their focus on healthcare not to the *quantity* of ser-vices being provided, but rather to the *quality or value* of those services [2].

Let's first take a look at the implementation of quantity-based productivity metrics in healthcare. Then we'll discuss moving beyond time-based productivity to a more value-based system.

Productivity and Its Industrialized Roots

Productivity is defined as "the rate per unit area or per unit volume at which a consumable ... is made by producers" [3].

So, how does this apply to healthcare?

Well, it seems that according to some healthcare consultants trained in Lean Six Sigma or other industry-based efficiency management pro-grams, clinicians convert inputs (time) into useful outputs (treatments/interventions). Many healthcare administrators, third-party payers, and other C-level executives (usually those holding MBAs and not clinical degrees or certifications) adopted this view of healthcare value creation or productive capacity.

However, this view of healthcare misses the mark. While at a basic level, clinicians do convert inputs into outputs through their work, the inputs and outputs defined above are wrong. Clinicians convert inputs (their specialized knowledge or expertise) into outputs (clinical and functional outcomes). The delivery of that expertise may be in the form of a treatment technique or intervention, or it could be delivered via consultation, advisement, or even coaching/guidance. Focusing only on the time-based treatment units as outputs misses the higher value provided by clinicians.

And, as I'll discuss in a bit, this time-based view of healthcare leaves clinicians feeling the squeeze. Clinics and clinicians feel they have to pump large volumes of patients through their doors and treatment programs to be "productive."

This, compounded by the fact that reimbursement for many healthcare services is based on the clinician's *time*—usually measured in treatment units—leads many healthcare organizations to become "treatment mills"; large warehouses delivering conveyor-belt assessment and treatment rather than truly individualized (and effective) care.

Productivity Versus Production

To understand how healthcare has arrived at its current position, we need to understand the whole idea of productivity versus production. As mentioned before, productivity refers to the efficiency of converting "inputs" to "outputs."

Well, how do you measure that in healthcare?

Healthcare—for the most part—is not based on products, but rather *services (based on specialized expertise and knowledge) and the "outputs" aren't tangible goods, but rather clinical outcomes.*

These inputs are also somewhat intangible.

Clinical skill, knowledge, and expertise are combined to deliver a service—often a treatment—to a customer (or patient), and it can be difficult to determine whether a standard amount of expertise or knowledge is being utilized in any given unit of treatment. Some patients are more complex than others, requiring more thinking, expertise, and knowledge translation on the part of the clinician. On top of that, some clinicians possess more specialized skills and knowledge in a given area than their peers. This means that they're able to achieve the same (or better) clinical outcomes in less time than a more novice or less experienced clinician.

On top of that, the "output" that we're talking about refers to a clinical or functional outcome, not a product. Sure, that outcome may be a result of an effective and individualized treatment program or plan of care, but those plans and programs (should) vary from patient to patient.

So, if a clinician applies years of clinical experience and expertise into developing a unique treatment plan for a patient experiencing chronic pain, regularly assesses and updates that plan as the patient progresses, and provides support and guidance throughout that treatment program, what is there to measure? And how do you ensure that measurement is standardized across varying clinicians, each with varying levels of clinical expertise?

Well, this conundrum has led many administrators, payers, and policy makers to measure the clinician's time (input) and the objective (measurable) output such as units of treatment, usually associated with a current procedural termionology (CPT) or treatment code.

That means when trying to measure "productivity," many healthcare administrators, third-party payers, and policy makers revert to measuring *time*. And, as mentioned earlier, the problem is that by measuring time, we fail to measure what truly matters.

What do we really care about in healthcare?

Do we care about how much *time* a clinician spends with a patient (time-based productivity)? Or, do we care about the actual *result* of that treatment (production)? The answer is most definitely the latter.

Quantity Versus Quality

I feel like I've said it enough, but it bears mentioning again: by focusing on time-based productivity measures, we miss what we truly should be assessing.

We want to measure the *quality* of the healthcare or service being provided.

The healthcare industry began focusing on time-based productivity because payers and policy makers conflated time spent with a patient with the quality or necessity of care. For example, a patient who received 90 minutes of physical therapy (PT) treatment in a day clearly required a higher level of care than a patient who only received 30.

Payers decided that they would pay clinicians based on the *time* they spent with a patient. I guess they thought that by structuring reimbursement in this way, they would incentivize clinicians and organizations to see more patients more efficiently. It actually created an incentive to see patients for a *longer* period of time than was necessary.

It became a game of quantity, sometimes at the expense of quality.

If a clinician gets reimbursed for the time he or she spends with a patient, what is more likely going to happen?

1. Will he or she spend an appropriate amount of time with each patient and see as many patients as possible in a day?
2. Or, will he or she try to get "the most" out of every patient interaction to cut down the number of notes and administrative time needed to document and bill for services?

The answer is clearly number 2. If given the choice, it's easier to see fewer patients for longer periods of time, regardless of need, because it means less administrative time.

I saw this happen as a lead clinician in an outpatient specialty clinic at a VA hospital. At the time, hospital management decided to focus on the number of treatment units billed per eight-hour tour of duty as a way to gauge clinician effectiveness. While this seemed to be a good idea at the time, six months later, when we went to review the data, we noticed that the number of unique social security numbers (a measure of how many individual patients were seen in each clinic) actually decreased over that six-month period.

By only measuring those time-based treatment codes, clinicians realized that all they had to do was maximize the treatment time with patients. They were able to see fewer patients per day and were still able to achieve their productivity requirements.

Tying Reimbursement to Productivity

This is precisely where it all went astray: when reimbursement became directly tied to the number of treatment units—or *time*—a clinician spends with a patient.

This shift fundamentally changed the dynamics of healthcare. Instead of incentivizing clinicians to be efficient and treat as many patients as

possible by seeing each for only the amount of time necessary, the opposite became the norm. Incentivized by this method of reimbursement, it
becomes more advantageous to see *fewer* patients for a *longer* period of
time. You end up with the same amount of revenue, with less administrative burden, documentation, and potential for billing or collections issues.

This also created an environment where healthcare organizations,
clinics, and hospitals began seeing clinicians as revenue producers that
needed to be squeezed for every available drop of revenue. This is typically
done by increasing productivity requirements for individual clinicians
and departments. Healthcare organizations bring in consultants with
certifications in Lean Six Sigma, project management, and operational
efficiency-building in an attempt to "maximize potential revenue" at
the facility.

Now, there's nothing wrong with trying to get the most bang for your
buck when it comes to the business and finance side of things. However, looking at healthcare through a solely industrial lens leaves healthcare organizations caught between the fancy spreadsheets from project
management initiatives and the all too evident reality that each patient is
uniquely different and, thus, won't fit into those projections or formulas.
Each patient may only vary in small amounts. One patient, for example,
may require 15 minutes of extra administrative (or nonproductive) time
to adequately provide appropriate care. Another may require additional
visits or treatments to achieve the benchmarked and expected clinical
outcomes. In a one-on-one or case-by-case management, these anomalies
and variables can easily be accounted for and managed in an efficient way.
However, if you're trying to operate at scale, those anomalies and variables
become "outliers" in the workflow.

Those outliers end up falling through the cracks, lost in bureaucratic
processes, or worse: simply falling into that "noncompliant" status. They
simply get tired of dealing with the steps, procedures, and bureaucracy,
and throw their hands up in the air.

Maximizing Productivity Through Policies and Procedures at the
Expense of Patient Care

I often saw this situation during my time at the VA. Veterans sought care
for an issue, sometimes for years on end, never truly receiving treatment

or intervention that benefited them. They bounced from clinic to clinic, from specialty office to specialty office. With each new consult or referral, they grew more anxious, irritated, and, ultimately, hopeless. By the time they arrived at my clinic for pain management or some kind of musculo-skeletal rehabilitation, they had that "let's get this over with" face.

After digging into their situation, it often became clear that this par-ticular patient just needed a simple procedure or consult. A common one we saw a lot in the outpatient specialty rehab clinic was referrals to a specialist like orthopedics. We saw many patients who had either been seen by orthopedics in the past and had discussed surgery or who had a notable need to be seen by an orthopedic MD. Because some consul-tants told the VA that requiring a six-to-eight-week rehab course of care prior to orthopedics would save $X and potentially prevent Y percent of unnecessary surgeries, the VA created a policy requiring that to take place prior to a patient receiving an orthopedic referral. And, in reality, that policy probably did prevent many patients from undergoing a premature surgical intervention.

The problem, however, ties into the topic we covered in Commit-ment #3. Often, the drive for efficiency that results from a fee-for-service or time-based reimbursement model drives healthcare organizations to implement policies and procedures aimed at improving that efficiency and maximizing revenue. So, when a patient comes along that doesn't fit nicely into that workflow, they often get lost in the bureaucratic maze of inaction.

So, going back to those veterans who we'd see in the clinic. They often simply needed a referral or consult to orthopedics. However, because of this policy—driven by the need to maximize efficiency in this time-based productivity-driven system—they found themselves unable to obtain that referral. They needed to go back into the queue, receive an evaluation in the rehab clinic, complete a course of care, and then—only after "failing conservative treatment"—they could receive a referral to orthopedics.

Oftentimes, because of circumstances outside of that veteran's con-trol, they were originally seen by orthopedics in previous years. They may have even had surgery scheduled. Then, either because of family or living circumstances, they had to cancel the procedure. They'd show up at their primary care office six months later and say that they wanted to follow up with orthopedics to reschedule the surgery. And, they were told that they needed to start the process over, in rehab, not with orthopedics. And thus, they cycled back into the standard workflow for the organization.

Now, in reality, throwing those patients back into the workflow costs the VA *more* money in the end, both in duplicating unnecessary (or ineffective) treatments, and also increasing the wait times (or limiting access) for veterans who may have actually benefited from treatment.

Again, I don't want it to sound like I'm saying to toss out all standard operating procedures. I kind of like having a framework from which to work. However, it should be just that: a framework, not a law carved into the stone facade of the organization. Sometimes, individual patient circumstances and situations may require stepping outside of the standardized workflows, not only to improve the quality of care but also to save time and financial resources.

Why Do We Get Paid?

Let's take a moment to briefly discuss the *why* behind all of this. All of the mess with policies, procedures, and time-based productivity stems from the underlying issue of payment and reimbursement. We need to understand for what clinicians and healthcare organizations are actually being paid.

Following the logic of the system we're currently in, you'd conclude that healthcare organizations and clinicians provide services or treatments. These treatments take a certain amount of time. And that time is reimbursed at a certain rate. Or, in the event of service-based reimbursement (nontimed CPT codes), the treatment or intervention itself is reimbursed at a certain rate.

As I've just laid out, this fee-for-service model shifted the entire healthcare industry into an environment where profits and financial solvency in some cases hinges on an organization's ability to maximize billable time. Because, in this environment, healthcare organizations get paid by the volume of treatments or interventions provided.

Here's the problem with that system: CLINICIANS DON'T GET PAID FOR TIME! They get paid for the value they create or the results they deliver. Time may be an "input" in that price equation, but healthcare organizations (and clinicians) don't get paid for that.

Jim Rohn used to say, "You don't get paid for your time. You get paid for the value you put into the time" [4].

Think about it: you pay a plumber to fix a leak, whether it takes him an hour or 10 minutes. You pay an HVAC company to make your AC blow cold. What you pay for is the *value* that professionals provide you with. How valuable is cold AC?

Well, here in the south where I live, it's pretty dang valuable. So, I'll pay an HVAC company $100 to come to fix my system. If it takes one hour, I'm happy. If it only takes 10 minutes, I'm *ecstatic*! And this leads us to some of the negative side effects of using time-based payment structures in healthcare.

What Payers and Patients Are Actually Buying

So, what about healthcare?

What are third-party payers and patients actually paying for?

What's the value they're hoping to gain from healthcare services?

As I've mentioned before, they're ultimately paying for an outcome.

Consider third-party payers like insurance companies or managed care organizations. Insurance companies pay healthcare providers for treatments and interventions that, over the long run, will improve the overall health of their beneficiaries. This, theoretically, leads to less healthcare spending over time. So, third-party payers aren't paying you for your treatment or CPT codes. They're paying you for future savings (and thus, increased profits). It's a cost-saving play.

Payers are not making any money off of the treatment clinicians provide to their beneficiaries directly. It's not like retail. They're not buying treatments at one rate and selling them to the patient at another. They pay a negotiated price or rate (again, a cost-savings play) to achieve their ultimate end goal of decreased overall spending, and increased profitability, in the future.

Patients, on the other hand, pay healthcare providers to apply their specialized expertise and knowledge to affect change or achieve some end goal. The goals and outcomes vary from patient to patient. Some patients want knowledge or insight about their condition and how to manage it better themselves. Others want a specific treatment or intervention (injections, surgery, and manual therapy) to relieve a symptom or improve a limitation. Either way, they don't necessarily pay for the treatment itself; or, the CPT code associated with that treatment.

They pay for the functional or clinical outcome.

This often gets missed by clinicians and healthcare organizations in today's world of high-volume, fee-for-service, billable time, and healthcare "at scale."

Understanding this, it becomes clear how this industrywide infatuation with fee-for-service reimbursement schemes, and all of the misaligned incentives and systemic problems they create, does little to actually move the needle on behalf of those who actually pay for our services.

Reimbursement arrangements should align with the interests of all stakeholders involved.

Negative Side Effects of Focusing on Time-Based Productivity

I already touched on one of the major downsides of focusing on time-based productivity and reimbursement but I want to explore this topic in a bit more depth. *Fee-for-service (especially time-based) payment models incentivize the lowest and slowest level of work for only minimally satisfactory quality.*

The reason is that time is the primary factor in this payment model. Time plays an overly-sized role, while completion or quality takes a back seat. As we discussed above, we don't—or shouldn't—be paid for our time.

As clinicians, we get paid for the value we put into the time or the outcome we produce. We possess specialized knowledge, skills, and tools that, when effectively applied to a patient's specific situation, deliver real outcomes like improved health, function, quality of life, and even decreased costs or healthcare expenditures in the future.

And, as mentioned earlier, that piece falls into the background in a fee-for-service payment model.

That's one of the reasons why there has been increasing focus on outcome measures (especially patient-driven measures) in healthcare—to make sure the time being spent is actually making a real difference.

It's also why Medicare has started shifting to things like Merit-based Incentive Payment Systems (MIPS). Other payers are also exploring different payment arrangements in the "value-based" spectrum: bundled payments, global service fees, and even shared savings programs.

Healthcare organizations and clinicians need to see this change coming, and what it means for the industry and their professions. By continuing to focus on (or worse, cling to) time-based productivity systems instead of outcomes, we place ourselves and our organizations at great risk once these industrywide trends become standardized across all payers and organizations.

We mustn't confuse activity with accomplishment if we're to effectively advocate for our professions, negotiate new payment arrangements with third-party insurers, and ultimately thrive in the new healthcare environment that is to come.

Where's the Value?

Given the face of a changing healthcare landscape coupled with uncertainties about the future, many administrators, consultants, and organizations have pushed metrics to measure clinician performance or value creation. Since most of these productivity measures and metrics are still based on the fee-for-service mentality, they often fail to represent the true value of a clinician's performance [5].

As mentioned above, many of these productivity measures calculate productivity—or value creation—as a function of time. But clinicians do much more than punch a time card for each patient they see. The value we create through our clinical expertise and treatment impacts the daily lives of the patients we serve.

Take someone who gets treated by a physical therapist for chronic LBP as an example. The patient comes in for treatment and is seen by a clinician for 54 minutes (four billable units). Can we really reduce the value of treatment to the number of billable units—or time—that the clinician spends with that patient?

Would that patient still be willing to pay the same price if the PT was able to effectively reduce his/her pain in half the time (say, 30 minutes)?

The answer is, in most cases, "yes."

Just like with the air conditioning example earlier in the chapter, patients come to therapy wanting and expecting an outcome. They've carved time out of their day to come into the clinic. In many cases, they want one thing: relief.

And *that* is the value that clinicians bring to the table. We as clinicians leverage our knowledge, clinical expertise, and skills to bring relief to patients that come to see us. The key to surviving, and thriving, as clinicians and healthcare organizations moving into the future lies in understanding what our customers (both payers and patients) truly want to receive or accomplish through us and how we can help them achieve those goals. Sure, we may provide treatments and interventions or other services that take time, but that's not what we get paid for. We get paid for the results those treatments and interventions yield in our customers' situations.

How Much Can You Get?

In addition to preventing healthcare organizations and clinicians from focusing on value, time-based reimbursement also places increasing pressure on organizations to push clinicians to "be productive." Again, if you're getting paid for your time, the only way to increase revenue is to increase the amount of *time* spent on billable activities.

Over the last 20 or so years, productivity requirements for staff clinicians continue to increase.

At one point, clinicians were expected to be 80 to 85 percent productive. That means that they spent about 80 to 85 percent of their time on direct patient care or billable activities. The remaining 15 to 20 percent of their time included administrative work, scheduling, communicating with patients or family members, and documentation. Now, that number has increased to at least 90 percent in most settings.

My first job as an Occupational Therapist required 95 percent productivity from its therapists. In an eight-hour day, that left us with 24 minutes total to complete all of the documentation required to bill for the services, follow up on outstanding issues such as splint or equipment orders, returning patient or family phone calls or messages, reviewing plans of care, and scheduling. This situation isn't uncommon, and it leaves clinicians with less time to do some of those things that may actually help the patient meet their goals or achieve their desired outcome.

This points to an important concept: *there is always an upper limit to the productive capacity of clinicians.*

Clinicians can only treat for a certain amount of time in a day. In an eight-hour day, that usually means roughly 456 minutes (95 percent of an eight-hour day, or 480 minutes).

Regardless of how *many* patients a clinician sees in a given day, time always constrains how *long* a clinician can spend on billable activities. This pushes many organizations to adopt an industrialized, conveyor-belt, approach to delivering care. Volume is the name of the game.

In my neck of healthcare, the physical medicine, and rehabilitation space, we see this a lot in PT franchises or chains. I won't name any names, but you know them. There are those clinics, or series of clinics, that appear on nearly every corner. They're like the waffle houses of the healthcare world.

As someone who also owns and operates a small, private PT/OT clinic, I often hear stories of "the other guys" from patients who end up receiving care from us. I hear about how the patient showed up for their first appointment and was seen in conjunction with one, or even two, other patients. The clinician, obviously under the pressure of management to maximize billable time, spent most of the initial evaluation with their nose glued to their computer screen so they could do their documentation during that appointment time. The patient received some standardized home exercise program handouts and was put on the schedule for a "plan of care," usually two times per week for six weeks. At the follow-up appointment, the patient got treated by another clinician, at the same time as two or three other patients. The clinician, desperate for time, bounced between each patient trying their best to provide individualized care. But, because of the workload, the patient ended up doing most of their exercises by themselves in the treatment gym. Maybe that clinician got around to providing some manual therapy or putting an ice pack on the patient at the very end of treatment, but at that point, the patient was ready to leave.

That "treatment," if you can call it that, wasted everyone's time. The clinician, firing on all cylinders, inched closer to burnout and apathy. And the patient likely received very little, if any benefit from the treatment and likely will continue with their pain or limitation, which also means that the payer (insurance company) didn't achieve their desired outcome of future cost savings.

That example alone is reason enough to consider changing the way we measure productivity and structure reimbursement in healthcare.

Benefits of Forgetting Time-Based Productivity

What could happen if we forget time-based productivity in healthcare?

What if we measured more than simply the time a clinician spent with a patient?

As I'll try and in the pages that follow, the changes to the overall effectiveness of healthcare services could improve greatly if we decoupled payment or reimbursement of healthcare services from the time-based, fee-for-service model under which we've been operating.

Untying reimbursement or payment from time, or even services, changes the incentives that drive clinicians and organizations. Changing the focus from time and units or codes returns the focus of healthcare to the patient and their unique situation and needs. Truly pricing healthcare services for the value they create or provide improves the revenue, efficiency, and impact of healthcare clinics and organizations.

Let's start with the incentive change created by paying clinicians for value or outcomes rather than time spent with a patient or procedures completed.

Incentives

As mentioned previously, healthcare is a service. Like any service, it takes time to complete, but the *outcome*s matter most. By reducing the payment structure to billable units of time or service-based procedure codes, clinicians and organizations adjust their treatment model to maximize the revenue and reduce unpaid activities (this is what led to time-based productivity measures in the first place).

I don't want to sound like I'm eluding to any nefarious intent, or insinuate that healthcare organizations are greedy, money-sucking machines whose goal is to maximize revenue without regard for the quality of care or clinical outcomes delivered to patients. Most clinics and organizations operate under this model now because that's how they get paid. They're simply operating under the confines of today's healthcare environment. Most clinicians, managers, and healthcare administrators know that there is a better way to deliver care. They just feel stuck in the current fee-for-service model.

Most clinicians and healthcare professionals intuitively understand that the current time-based or procedure-based reimbursement structure does not fully capture or define the *value* that their services provide to patients, their significant others, the healthcare system, and society at large [6]. What fee-for-service reimbursement actually does—as mentioned earlier—is incentivize clinicians to spend more time delivering mediocre or unnecessary treatments in an effort to maximize billable time.

However, when paid by the job—call it value-based payment or reimbursement—clinicians become incentivized to be efficient and effective. This may mean that a clinician actually spends *less* time with a patient while delivering equal or greater results. After all, if they get paid the same amount for the treatment, regardless of time, wouldn't they want to provide the most efficient (quickest) treatment option available?

Here's a hypothetical example below.

Time or Procedure Versus Task

Since my clinical background is rooted in outpatient orthopedic rehabilitation, it's easier for me to express this idea in the form of a clinical example from practice. Let's take frozen wrist as an example of what could happen if clinicians were reimbursed for a treatment outcome rather than the time they spent completing various treatments.

Typically, when someone is referred to outpatient therapy to "improve ROM" for a "stiff wrist" following injury or surgery, that person is seen multiple times a week for 45- to 60-minute treatment sessions. But, as I'll explain in a bit, the decision to set treatment times at 45 to 60 minutes has more to do with maximizing reimbursement than clinical necessity. Other treatment options exist that require significantly less time and provide arguably equal or better clinical outcomes.

For example, Draper showed in a 2010 article that six minutes of ultrasound followed by 10 minutes of wrist mobilizations and 20 minutes of ice could result in a return to normal active range of motion (AROM) in just six treatments [7]. Now, I don't know about you, but six treatments that only last around 36 minutes sounds a lot better than four-to-six weeks of two treatments a week for 60 minutes each. Now, I'm not going to get into the ins-and-outs of the research around ultrasound, manual therapy, and the like. I know there are differing opinions in literature. This example just helps me illustrate my point. You can find this type of example with nearly every treatment procedure or technique.

I'll explain a bit more about this later but, under most current reimbursement structures, a clinician can't bill for six minutes of ultrasound, because it is less than eight minutes—the threshold for a 15-minute charge. That means the clinician has to make a choice: either forgo the ultrasound treatment altogether, or deliver an additional two minutes to the patient to reach that eight-minute threshold. Now, two minutes may not sound like a lot. However, two minutes per treatment code or procedure multiplied by 10 patients per day, five days a week, for four weeks each month, and you're looking at 400 minutes of treatment per clinician, per month that is essentially wasted providing superfluous treatments in order to reach billing thresholds. At 36 minutes per treatment, that clinician would have been able to see an additional 10 to 11 patients that month.

By changing the payment structure to a values-based or treatment-based system, we free up clinicians to provide treatments like the one above. That could result in more patients receiving treatment and potentially experiencing higher-quality clinical outcomes.

Focus

Now let's take a look at what happens to the *focus* of healthcare and treatment delivery when we forget about time-based or procedure-based productivity measurements.

We've all been there: a patient walks into the clinics and we think, "how am I going to get four units out of them?" It happens to every clinician at some point. Blame it on administration, management, or policies.

The reality is that, when fee-for-service-based productivity measures are the main Key Performance Indicator (KPI) monitored by an organization, clinicians begin to see patients as walking treatment units. They forget about taking the time to dive into their unique circumstance and recovery journey. They simply want to make sure that they hit their 29 units for the day (90 percent productivity for an eight-hour day).

What happens when that incentive is removed?

What happens when clinicians are measured not by how many treatment *units* they complete in a day, but by how much *value* they provide in a day?

That might sound like the same thing, especially in today's world where the value seems inherently tied to the quantity of medical procedures completed. But as we'll discuss in a little bit, they're vastly different. When clinicians no longer have to worry about counting minutes with patients, they can actually deliver the most valuable treatment option for that unique patient.

Take another look at the example of a frozen wrist as shown earlier. A clinician that doesn't have to worry about hitting an eight-minute threshold for ultrasound, combined with 45 minutes of other treatment techniques (to hit the magical 53 minutes to bill for four units) can focus on delivering what that patient *actually* needs. Nothing more. Nothing less.

We change the focus of healthcare from time and numbers to the people in our clinics and what *they* need to recover, not what *we* need to maximize billing codes.

Revenue and the Bottom Line

What happens to revenue if we leave behind the fee-for-service mindset?

Well, I think the case can be made that you may actually see an *increase* in revenue at an organizational level while also delivering more efficient, cost-effective care to payers and patients alike. In a world where time or procedure quantity does not dictate reimbursement, clinics may actually be able to earn more money and spend more time providing meaningful treatment.

As an example, let's look at a value-based reimbursement model. I'll expand on the specifics of this type of reimbursement model later in the chapter, but here are the basics: this type of model typically involves the clinic charging a fee for a treatment session or entire course of care, not charging per service or per treatment code. Many out-of-network or cash-based clinics I have worked with operate under this type of payment model.

Using the aforementioned frozen wrist example, let's say a patient comes to the clinic for a treatment session. The clinic receives an equivalent of $100 per treatment. The clinician completes that previously mentioned therapeutic ultrasound (six minutes), manual wrist mobilizations (10 minutes), and applies ice (20 minutes). Total treatment time: 36 minutes, less if the patient opted for the ice at home or on the way back to work. For a 36-minute treatment, the clinic earns $100 (the rate equivalent per treatment).

It also means that the clinic can provide more one-on-one care to each patient in the clinic. Since they can cut out the fluff needed to reach billing thresholds, they can provide patients with the most effective portions of treatment without the pressure to greatly increase patient volume. This factor alone leads to physicians spending an average of seven minutes with each patient or physical therapists seeing two patients simultaneously. By requiring less time to deliver effective treatments to each patient, clinics can see patients per day, while delivering more individualized care in that time frame, all while increasing the possible revenue available in an eight-hour day.

Value Versus Time-Based Reimbursement

Now let's contrast a value-based reimbursement model with a standard fee-for-service model. Say that our patient with a frozen wrist has Medicare. The reimbursement, without adding in additional time to reach billing thresholds, would break down like this:

- Ultrasound (97035): $14.06 (but really $0, since six minutes is less than the minimum of eight)

- Manual Therapy (97140): $31.10 (one unit, since it was only 10 minutes)
- Ice (97010): $0 (not reimbursed by Medicare)

These rates were taken from the 2019 physician fee schedule calculator available at the Centers for Medicare and Medicaid Services (CMS) website. So, for the exact same treatment that would have been delivered under a value-based reimbursement model, the clinic only receives $45.16—actually, only $31.10 since the United States doesn't qualify under the eight-minute rule—for that treatment from Medicare. As you can see this incentivizes clinics to routinely provide services above and beyond what a patient truly needs. Because if they only provide what is necessary, they go broke.

Main Takeaway

We all need to remember that healthcare is about one thing: *the patient.*

The reason we have jobs is that patients need our help and treatment in order to achieve improved health, overcome injuries or disabilities, and continue living out their meaningful roles in society.

The reason most of us chose healthcare as a career was to help people get better. We felt a calling to serve our fellow human beings, to help them overcome injuries or pain, or to improve their health and well-being. Our job as healthcare professionals is a big deal! And it provides tremendous value to all stakeholders in the healthcare world.

However, our current fee-for-service reimbursement and revenue model doesn't help us to achieve those ends. Incentivizing healthcare organizations to focus metrics and KPIs on time-based or procedure-based productivity reduces patients to numbers. It incentivizes slower work of lower quality or a higher volume of unnecessary or low-value procedures. Clinicians burn out trying to hit productivity numbers and running patients through cookie-cutter treatment protocols. We lose the human—or person-to-person—experience and service that healthcare should be.

Perhaps, we need to take another look at how we measure productivity, reimbursement, and service delivery, and return the focus back to the patient and their needs.

How to Move Beyond Time-Based Productivity and Fee-For-Service Payment Models

Let's say you're on board with the idea that time-based productivity and reimbursement lead to clinician burnout, decreased patient engagement, and reduced patients to numbers on a spreadsheet. You agree that something needs to change. What you measure, how you measure it, and where you focus need to consider the end-user or recipient of the healthcare services: the patient.

How do you do that?

What metrics or data do you focus on?

What reimbursement or payment structures do the most to deliver value to patients rather than treatment units?

Historically, reimbursement schemes and even healthcare policy view value in healthcare as some function of dollars spent versus objective measures or outcomes. This is likely due to the fact that most research and discussion around value for healthcare services and reimbursement for treatment stems from either payer or policy maker organizations. Healthcare regulators and policy makers at the CMS drive much of the discussion around how much providers should be paid, how to track and price healthcare services, and restrictions on how those services are delivered. Likewise, third-party payers like insurance companies also establish policies and norms regarding how services should be delivered and how they will be paid.

However, as I mentioned at the end of the chapter on communicating value, healthcare involves at least four distinct parties or stakeholders. Those stakeholders include the payer, the policy maker, the provider, and the patient. I've heard this referred to as "the four Ps of healthcare." I'm not sure who came up with that phrase, but I like alliteration and it makes the concept easy to remember.

The problem then, in determining the best way to assess, price, and pay for healthcare services, is the varying incentives and priorities of each stakeholder. The fact that, as an industry, we lack a shared understanding or vernacular for discussing value also contributes to this confusion [8].

Now, let's go back to the underlying problem: in healthcare, most of the discussion about payment and value comes from policy makers and payers. Now one could argue that those two stakeholders have more to lose from a financial perspective. They bear a large administrative cost for regulation and monitoring of the industry and also a direct cost through paying for healthcare services.

However, patients and providers also have a lot on the line. Especially in a world of rising healthcare costs in the form of premiums, deductibles, and coinsurances/copayments, a patient now shoulders a larger portion of the direct cost of healthcare. Declining reimbursement rates in the fee-for-service model result in clinicians (providers) resorting to high-volume, often low-value, treatment or services in an effort to simply stay afloat in the financially turbulent times of the day.

A world where true, value-based healthcare models exist then, must balance each of the incentives, priorities, and perspectives of these four stakeholders in order to arrive at a system that is acceptable. The goal shouldn't be perfection—no system involving this much complexity ever is perfect—but rather, "acceptable."

Often, when I have discussions with colleagues and others in the healthcare industry, any potential solution or proposed system to replace our current model meets the all-too-common criticism of "not being perfect." Unfortunately, in real life, any proposed reimbursement scheme involves trade-offs—and the risk of potentially negative impacts—in an attempt to create a system that, on the balance, delivers the greatest possible benefit with the lowest possible risk or negative side effects. I am not an economist, and I don't possess any advanced or terminal degree in public health or healthcare policy. What follows includes simply my opinions and ideas regarding healthcare payment, pricing, and how to avoid some of the pitfalls of our current system.

What's Wrong With Fee-For-Service Reimbursement?

Odds are that your clinic or organization gets paid based on the number of treatment units (or time) billed during each patient appointment. While on the surface this sounds logical and fair—you get paid for the time you spend delivering care to a patient—the reality is that this arrangement doesn't truly capture the value of what your clinic and clinicians provide to your patients.

As previously discussed, time-based reimbursement incentivizes the slowest and lowest quality work acceptable. It incentivizes clinicians and organizations to see a lower number of patients for a longer period of time, in those cases where payment is linked to time-based codes. In situations where payment is linked to service-based codes, providers become incentives to see an ever-larger number of patients on a given day. This leaves some patients getting far more treatment time than what evidence or research would indicate, or some patients receiving less time than they would like from their clinician who is trying to see 50 patients a day. Regardless of which method you choose, a time-based or a service-based reimbursement, this fee-for-service model results in patients feeling unsatisfied with the treatment they receive and clinicians feeling burnt out due to the increasing work demands.

This system also causes clinicians and organizations to see patients as numbers of potential "treatment units" rather than unique individuals on a road to recovery. That leads many organizations to develop "standardized operational procedures" aimed at efficiently delivering a standardized treatment protocol to the largest number of patients possible. Again, because this model came from the perspective of payers and policy makers, it omits and doesn't account for the perspectives of providers or patients.

I won't belabor this point any further since it was covered earlier in this chapter, but I think it's important to understand it. The way healthcare reimbursement is set up today results in clinician burnout, reduced efficiency of care, and lower patient engagement and satisfaction. If we truly care about improving healthcare delivery and quality while at the same time reducing cost and improving clinical outcomes, we need to find a way to break the link between reimbursement and time or the quantity of procedures billed. This idea has become widely prominent. In fact, many opinions, research, and business strategies point to a healthcare future in which healthcare services are chosen, delivered, and reimbursed (or paid for) within a value-based framework as opposed to a fee-for-service model [8].

How Do We Forget Time-Based Productivity Metrics and Move Away From Fee-For-Service Reimbursement Models?

This is where the rubber meets the road so to speak. It's easy to talk about the negative effects of time-based productivity and fee-for-service reimbursement. It's also easy to say that healthcare needs to focus on each individual patient.

Lord knows I've sat through those "healthcare leadership" seminars or courses that focus on creating "unique patient experiences" or "individualizing healthcare treatment." On the surface, these seminars sound interesting, but a few minutes in, you realize that you're about to hear the same old, nonspecific ideas that you've heard at the past 10 seminars you've attended.

So, *how* do we implement those changes?

More importantly, *why* does it seem that while everyone knows that something needs to change, we rarely see follow-through or action?

I think the answers to those questions lie in the fact that, on the surface, the solution seems impossible. As I discussed earlier, healthcare involves four distinct stakeholders, each of which has differing priorities and incentives. And then, there's the whole "inertia" idea. As humans, we are very averse to change. Cognitive biases, like loss aversion or fear of the unknown, prevent us from making decisions that we may intuitively know may be beneficial.

That being said, you can't fully move away from time-based productivity without also moving away from time-based reimbursement models. And that itself sounds like you might as well try scaling Mount Everest in your swimming trunks.

In addition, changing payment or reimbursement models will have a real and meaningful impact on both providers and payers alike. Value-based reimbursement models render high-volume healthcare business practices inefficient and, in some cases, hugely unprofitable.

Now, while it may seem impossible, I'd like to propose a few simple ideas clinics and organizations can use to begin moving away from time-based productivity and reimbursement within a fee-for-service model. And then, I'll also explore a few value-based reimbursement models and how they've been implemented.

I believe that just making small, incremental changes toward the world we want to see, is better than throwing our hands up in defeat. Some of these ideas come from my time in the VA Healthcare system, my work in the private practice world, consulting projects I've been involved in, and some ideas that have already been put into practice across the United States. We'll start with metrics and move on to payment models after that.

Metrics

If you can't measure it, you can't improve it.

—Peter Drucker

Managers and administrators everywhere try and measure or gauge performance. That's part of their function within the organization. Healthcare is no different.

The performance of staff, performance of products or services, and even financial performance all receive the attention of those in executive offices. This is understandable since monitoring performance in these areas helps management make improvements. However, many healthcare organizations and clinics go astray by overly focusing on time-based productivity or utilization measurements. While this gives a general understanding of how *much* a clinician or clinic produces in a given day—based on treatment units—this data doesn't show the true *value* or *efficiency* of that clinician or clinic.

For example, in a time-based world, productivity is measured by taking the actual number of treatment minutes provided in a given day and dividing it by the available number of treatment units (480 for an eight-hour day) to get a percentage. For example, a clinician achieves 90 percent productivity if he or she spends 432 minutes a day completing direct, billable patient care activities. While this is useful information, it leaves out many important factors that would help to improve care and efficiency.

By solely focusing on time-based productivity, organizations miss the opportunity to make improvements that affect patient engagement, clinical outcomes, and patient satisfaction. If we want to improve the quality of healthcare delivery while also reducing cost and improving patient experience, we need to look at more than just treatment units. Some organizations have begun to incorporate other metrics when evaluating clinician or clinic performance. Below are a few of these areas.

Utilization

When I worked in the VA Healthcare system, I had the opportunity to be part of a project with the executive team involving different ways to measure the performance of the Rehabilitation Service Line. Many ideas floated around the room during some of the initial meetings, but one thing became clear: we wanted to be able to measure more than just how many units an individual clinician or clinic produced in a day.

We wanted to be able to know how many patients were being treated, how often they were treated, how long they were treated, how long their courses of care were, and the availability of appointments in these clinics.

We settled on *Clinic Utilization* as our performance measures going forward. This involved several key changes over simple productivity. Instead of focusing only on the number of treatment units or treatment minutes provided by clinicians on a given day, we focused instead on the combination of treatment units and unique social security numbers seen by each clinician or clinic (we also looked at availability, treatment duration, and so on).

Why was clinic utilization much more effective at measuring efficiency, quality, and value provided by our clinics? Because the focus of the data measurement involved more than just the *time* a clinic or clinician spent treating in a given day, week, or month. By focusing on how many unique patients came through a given clinic in a week, we were able to determine whether our clinics and clinicians were providing efficient, high-quality care, or if they were simply bringing in the same patients in for extended—often unnecessary—treatments to hit their productivity numbers.

This, combined with an audit of available appointments—we randomly checked every 7th appointment slot on a clinician's schedule—helped us evaluate more than simply the number of treatment units or treatment minutes. It gave us insight into *how*, *when*, and *where* those treatments were being delivered. Given the information we gathered from that data, we made changes on a clinic-by-clinic basis to improve access, decrease wait times, and improve the quality of care being delivered.

And, all of this was done under the standard fee-for-service paradigm. We didn't have to tackle the reimbursement animal to make those changes.

Clinical Outcomes

Another key metric that should be monitored in any healthcare setting—and usually is—involves clinical outcomes. We see this a lot in marketing and advertising for different healthcare organizations and clinics. These metrics are used to convince patients to use that particular facility for whatever service.

But, can we use clinical outcomes or clinical effectiveness measures as a component or factor of productivity tracking?

What can clinical outcomes tell us about a clinic's or clinician's efficiency or productive capacity?

Obviously, many factors influence the outcomes experienced by patients (reread Chapter 1 on the BSP model to learn about that). Even still, one major factor regularly impacts patient outcomes: the treatment plan and delivery. This may seem obvious, but *how* a certain treatment is delivered has a major impact on the results patient's experience, expectations, and clinical outcomes. By incorporating clinical outcomes into clinician or clinic performance measures, we gain some insight into this dynamic of healthcare delivery.

For example, I've worked with clients who began using standardized objective measures, such as a QuickDASH assessment (Disability of the Shoulder and Hand), to track individual clinician effectiveness. Typically, this was done by measuring the average change in standardized measures for a specific clinician over a period of time. Now, this system has its problems, and it's not perfect? I mean, how many factors outside of a clinician's control affect clinical outcomes? But, it's an interesting idea to ponder.

Patient-Driven Outcomes

In a world where metrics, numbers, and percentages seem to drive healthcare decisions, patients often feel forgotten. They see themselves being run through the "steps" of treatment, without any real consideration for their own goals, desires, or values. To combat this, some healthcare clinics and organizations have begun using patient-centered or patient-driven outcome measures to assess the quality of their healthcare service delivery. For example, some research suggests that measures associated with overall health, sleep, fatigue, physical function, and mental health should be used when treating patients with rheumatoid arthritis [9].

Obviously, including these measures improves a patient's experience and engagement throughout the treatment plan. But, do these measures benefit the clinic or organization?

I would argue that including patient-driven measures is not only beneficial but will also be vital for healthcare organizations entering the new healthcare environment. Everyone from private sector organizations to the CMS has been saying that value-based or merit-based payment and reimbursement systems are coming (more on that to follow). Healthcare organizations that begin including patient-driven measures now will be better poised to thrive in this new environment.

One patient-driven outcome measure, the CAREs Measurement Tool is a simple, 10-question questionnaire that measures empathy in the context of patient interactions [1]. It is free to use and comes with normative data for benchmarking and tracking. Utilizing a simple, quick-to-administer measure like this provides organizations with valuable information at both a clinic or departmental level as well as for individual clinicians. This data can help guide quality improvement initiatives which can improve efficiency and quality of care being delivered, all while maintaining a patient-centered mindset.

This type of tracking also provides organizations or clinics with valuable marketing material that can lead to business growth and expansion going forward. For example, let's say that a patient is looking for a PT clinic to treat his/her lower back pain. There are two PT clinics within a 10-minute drive from their workplace. Both clinics seem to be staffed with knowledgeable and trained clinicians. However, clinic A's website and material focus on their process, treatments offered, and the like. Clinic B's website and material highlight how their treatment process involves and includes patient-driven outcomes. Clinic B's website even has testimonials from patients talking about how clinic B took the time to listen to them, customize the treatment plan, and worked with their patients to help improve on those factors mentioned above (sleep, function, and so on). Which clinic will the patient choose? I think it's pretty obvious.

Alternative Payment Models

As mentioned earlier in this chapter, many of the metrics that have sprung up around healthcare stem from the reimbursement and payment model that dominates the landscape (at least in the United States). For the most part, health insurance companies and government payers alike reimburse clinicians and healthcare organizations based on the number of "treatment units" billed during each visit. Nearly all of these treatment units relate either to time or service.

For example, in the PT world, 97140 (manual therapy) is a treatment code that is billed in 15-minute units. If a physical therapist does 27 minutes of manual therapy, they bill two units of 97140 and the insurance company pays them for two units. As discussed, the incentives created by this reimbursement model cause all kinds of problems from clinician burnout to lower patient outcomes. I'm assuming if you've read this far, that you don't need any further convincing on this point.

So, the question is this: how can organizations and clinicians step away from fee-for-service reimbursement to improve outcomes for both patients and clinicians?

I've found that an effective strategy is to begin to implement or offer alternative payment models, build that portion of the business (which reduces the revenue from traditional payment sources), and get to the point where those alternative payment models make up the majority of revenue. It doesn't have to be all or nothing. Consider it a sliding scale. Some clinics will be able to move to 100 percent non-fee-for-service payment, while some find that 15 to 25 percent is their sweet spot. However, since we know that the fee-for-service model will go the way of the dodo bird within our lifetime, it helps to begin planning for and utilizing these "nontraditional" reimbursement sources in practice.

What follows is a quick breakdown and discussion of a few different alternative payment models that veer from the fee-for-service schemes most commonly seen today. Now, this topic could fill its own book, so this will by no means be an exhaustive list or even a fully comprehensive discussion. My aim is to simply broach the topic.

Private-Pay Reimbursement

When thinking about alternatives to traditional, insurance-based payment models, the first one that comes to mind tends to be cash or private pay. Using this type of payment model, a clinician or organization offers healthcare services and simply charges the patient instead of the insurance company.

Often, these organizations supply the patient with a "super bill" that the patient can submit to his/her insurance company for reimbursement. Sometimes, if the patient is a member of a health share organization, these costs can be directly reimbursed by the health share either to the patient, or the provider. While this solves the clinic's headache of dealing with insurance companies in a time of declining reimbursement and increasing denials of coverage, nothing much changes in the treatment that patients receive.

In fact, I'm going to go out on a limb and say that—if all the clinic is doing is shifting the payment source from the insurance company to the patient—this model may actually increase the cost of care for the patient without any notable improvement in quality or outcomes.

Now I realize that many clinics that offer private pay or cash-based services offer some discounts to patients who opt to pay in that way. In that case, it may be beneficial for patients to choose that option simply due to cost. However, isn't the goal to improve the quality of healthcare while decreasing the cost?

If that's the case, then we need to look at changes to more than just who pays the bills.

Value-Based Payment Models

Another term that gets thrown around in this arena is *value-based* payment. This often gets confused with global fees or cash-pay rates similar to those we will discuss in Packaged Services because they appear similar, and the terms get used interchangeably.

I argue that there is—or at least, should be—a notable difference between cash-based and value-based payment models. As noted earlier, cash-based or private-pay simply shifts the upfront financial responsibility to the patient. In the end, it still involves a clinician or clinic billing for treatment codes and units (especially if they supply their patients with super bills to submit to their insurance companies). How does this change anything? It still bases payment for healthcare on time. And, as we've discussed, time-based payment is what we want to move away from.

Value-based pay, on the other hand, isn't based on the *time* a clinician spends with a patient. Instead, it bases the fee on a variety of factors such as time, outcomes, or complexity. In a word, the overall value of that treatment. Ultimately, isn't that the goal?

Now, these become difficult to develop because, as mentioned previously, four stakeholders exist in this space, so any value-based payment model needs to balance the perspectives and priorities of each.

Healthcare payers should focus on *value and efficiency*. Clinicians should be paid independent of the time spent with patients. This incentivizes those clinicians to be efficient in their treatment delivery while delivering the highest value possible. In the next section, we'll talk a little bit about packaged services, subscriptions, and lump-sum payments as a way to move closer to true value-based reimbursement models.

Packaged Service Fees and Subscriptions

Now, in the private-pay market, some clinics and organizations have begun to offer packaged services. Instead of a fee-for-service model, where the patient either pays per appointment or pays some discounted amount from a traditionally-billed visit, the patient pays for an entire course of care (or the treatment package).

This has gained traction specifically in allied health specialties, though hospital systems are now entering the game here. Physical therapists or chiropractors, for example, may offer patients a variety of treatment "packages." These packages may include a number of treatments or visits, access to a clinician via secure platforms, and other services not covered by traditional payers.

Global Fees

Healthcare systems and hospitals have also begun offering these types of services. For example, my wife and I have five (at the time of this writing) children. For the last three deliveries, we have not had traditional health insurance, but rather have been members of a health share organization. This means that we do not have traditional insurance coverage and are essentially "private-pay" or self-pay patients.

So, when we arrived at our first appointment with the OB, we paid a single, global fee. That covered us for all of the prenatal appointments, labs, ultrasounds, delivery, and postnatal appointments. One, single fee. The same was true of the hospital. We paid one, single global delivery fee that covered the hospital stay, anesthesia, pediatrician visit, postnatal checks, and so on, while we were in the hospital.

Now, our health share covered most of those fees. So, my wife and I paid about $1,000 or so, and the rest was "shareable" and we were either reimbursed for those expenses, or the health share directly paid to the providers. Either way, for about the cost of a traditional insurance-based deductible, we received the care we needed.

In addition, the hospital and providers received their payment *upfront.* The revenue wasn't spread out over the months of appointments, visits, and hospital stays. I'm sure most healthcare administrators would agree that getting paid upfront definitely helps with cash flow at any organization.

Packaged Service Offerings

Another way of offering global fees can be packaged service options. At the clinic that I own and operate, we offer "packaged" service offerings that include secure messaging, asynchronous telehealth, telehealth visits, and/or in-person or in-clinic treatment options. We developed a few different options and patients without insurance, or who elect to act as self-pay, find much more flexibility in receiving their care than they would in a traditional fee-for-visit model. You can check out how we structured those packages here: https://pro-activehealth.com/packages/. Now, while

I know these options are by no means perfect, it's a step in the right direction, and we try to update them as we received feedback from patients.

Subscriptions and Direct Primary Care

We actually developed those packages while working with some providers who engage in another variation of payment: subscription. Particularly, I'm talking about direct primary care (DPC) groups. These groups charge patients a flat, monthly fee (like a subscription) which gives the patients access to the providers, appointments, and, sometimes, discounted rates on pharmaceuticals or other providers. This type of arrangement truly places the patient–clinician relationship at the center of the entire transaction. The patient is paying directly for care, so they are going to be more discerning about where their dollars are going, and whether the continued subscription is a valuable use of those dollars. The clinician, therefore, is incentivized to make the experience, and the value they deliver, so great that the patient agrees that the subscription fee is worth it. This leads direct PCPs to offer many more preventative and wellness offerings that may not always be covered by traditional insurance-based business models.

Global Treatment Fees

Moving into the future, great opportunities exist in incorporating these types of "packaged" service offerings, not only to private individuals but also to healthcare systems and insurers or payers. For example, I know of some healthcare groups that have gone to a workman's comp company with an offering that included a global fee for a given diagnosis. That global fee covered the entire course of care, regardless of how many visits or treatments were delivered. This incentivized the provider to deliver the most effective care, in order to achieve the desired outcomes in a financially sustainable manner. Again, it incentivized truly person-centered care.

At the clinic I own, ProActive Rehabilitation and Wellness, we participate with payers in a few programs that involve a global service fee. Here's how it works: the patient receives a referral for PT or OT. We then complete an initial evaluation, documenting the patient's specific situation and limitations. We send that to the insurance provider who categorizes that patient's condition into a "care level." Each care level corresponds to a certain global fee for that condition. We receive authorization to treat that patient for a specific time frame. After that, no further reimbursement is provided. We can see the patient one time or 100 times within that time frame or treatment window and it won't affect our reimbursement. We can use traditional treatment methods or nontraditional (like asynchronous telehealth tools) without worrying about reimbursement. We've already received our global fee, so we can use whatever treatment techniques or tools we have at our disposal to help the patient achieve their desired outcomes.

Now there are problems with these types of models. For one thing, the process of rating or categorizing a patient's status based on a diagnosis code and results from outcome measures leaves much to be desired, in my opinion. Again, every person is uniquely different, so there are instances, and we have dealt with them in the clinic, where a person may have a "simple diagnosis" but the raters don't or can't consider other psycho-social factors affecting that patient's condition into their categorization. So, these patients end up being placed in a lower category than what is truly needed to achieve their desired outcomes. But, I firmly believe that as technology improves and more payers enter this space, we'll be able to iron out some of the wrinkles in these early attempts at global payment options.

Benefits of Moving Beyond Time-Based Productivity and Reimbursement

Before wrapping up, I'd like to take some time to go over the benefits of making some of these decisions and moving away from time-based productivity metrics (and ultimately fee-for-service models). Deciding to begin implementing and including alternative payment methods—or even just changing metrics—involves hurdles for both individual clinicians and organizations as a whole. Below, I'll outline a few benefits for both patients and clinicians that can be found in the switch away from time-based healthcare. Again, there are four stakeholders in any value discussion in healthcare. This only examines the perspectives of the two.

Benefits to Patients

Healthcare is about one thing: people. Behind all the research, evidence, protocols, measurements, outcomes, and payments lie people. Healthcare is people helping people; helping them heal, recover, and return to their desired activities and goals.

So, what benefits can patients experience with a change from time-based productivity and reimbursement?

To start, patients that pay value-based costs for healthcare receive transparent pricing. How many times do patients get treatment, pay their copays, and think they are done, only to receive a bill later? This leaves patients feeling frustrated and can even result in lower patient satisfaction survey results. As Paul Potter has pointed out, this setup also protects the integrity of the patient–clinician relationship [10]. By removing the effects of third-party payer constraints such as coding and billing out of the equation, patients and clinicians are able to collaborate on the best (or most preferred) plan of care without the risk of denial from payers. This allows for truly patient-centered (or patient-driven) treatment plans. Whether this is accomplished through global service fees, packaged offerings, or subscription models, working outside of the fee-for-service billing system allows clinicians to offer services and treatments that may not be covered by those payers.

Costs may also decline under these value-based payment models. For example, a recently published study showed preliminary evidence suggesting that cash-based treatment can be more cost-effective than the traditional insurance-based payment [11]. These findings also suggested comparable clinical outcomes. Who wouldn't want to pay less for the same outcomes? (It would be interesting to study the difference—if any—between cash-based and value-based payment models on clinical outcomes like global service fees.)

Another great benefit to patients under a cash or value-based payment model is the fact that all patients are welcome. Especially if the clinic offers these options outside of the traditional payment models, they are free to see whichever patient wishes to be seen. In short, all patients are approved; with insurance, without insurance, in-network, or out-of-network. Again, this provides transparency, control, and ultimately the choice to patients when selecting healthcare providers.

Benefits to Clinicians

Besides the benefits to patients listed above, cash-based or value-based payment models in healthcare also offer enticing benefits to clinicians. Here is a quick list that attracts clinics and clinicians to these types of payment models:

- More Autonomy
- Less Conveyor-Belt Treatment
- Less Bureaucracy and Red Tape
- Feeling More Valued and Valuable
- Better Treatment Options

Typically, clinicians working in traditional, fee-for-service-based healthcare organizations feel like cogs in a giant machine. They feel forced to see patients stacked one on top of the other, cranking them through cookie-cutter treatment protocols. They constantly need to send more paperwork; justify this and provide reasoning for that. They often feel that they know what the most effective treatment option may be, but are prevented from offering it because of insurance denials or approvals.

Much of this goes away with these alternative payment models. Clinicians are able to spend sufficient time with each patient, providing the most-effective treatment. Without the need to "squeeze more units" out of each patient—or stack them on top of each other—the risk of clinician burnout diminishes. Since there are no approval processes, these clinicians have more freedom to select treatment plans they feel would be best for each patient, without having to deal with any bureaucratic approval processes.

Summary

At the end of the day, any move toward more patient choice, clinician autonomy, and more effective treatment helps everyone: payers, providers, policy makers, and patients. While it may seem impossible to completely change the healthcare system, each clinician and organization can take small, incremental steps toward shifting the focus of healthcare productivity and payment away from time and toward value.

Value-based measures and payment models benefit both clinicians and patients, and can potentially reduce costs while improving clinical outcomes. While some of these value-based payment models suffer from the growing pains of early development, they hold the potential to free the healthcare industry from this fee-for-service model, which everyone can agree has major flaws.

Ultimately, healthcare is a human (person-to-person) service and experience that cannot be adequately measured by treatment units or time segments. We should all strive to implement processes and systems that move the focus of healthcare back to people.

CHAPTER 8

Commitment #8

Lead Our Patients

We will lead our patients and guide them through the treatment process toward achieving their desired outcomes and goals.

I was once giving a lecture to a group of graduate occupational therapy (OT) students. The subject was balancing the leadership role of the clinicians with client-centered or individualized patient care. One student asked a question to the effect of, "What if the patient already knows what's wrong with them and they just want you to provide the specific treatment?" Here is my response:

Are you a licensed, expert clinician, or a vendor? Are your services and treatment plans "off the shelf" or "one size fits most"? Do you lead your patients, or do you take orders like a waiter?

Most clinicians worth their salt would respond, "Absolutely not! We develop individualized treatment programs for each patient." In reality, many clinicians strive for that level of patient-centered care. We learn in school the importance of "individualized" or "patient-centered" care. Research shows that patient-centered and individualized treatment plans yield better outcomes and results.

However, sometimes, clinicians find themselves being driven by their patients. They allow the patient's desires, expectations, and views to overly influence the course of treatment. Sometimes, this stems from poor communication at the beginning of treatment. The patient's expectations are not addressed and, rather than deal with an unhappy patient (or negative online reviews), the clinician decides to placate the patient.

The problem with this is that it doesn't necessarily prevent the patient from leaving bad reviews or ending up dissatisfied with treatment. In fact, these patients are more likely to have a negative experience. By allowing them to take the leadership role, whenever it must be taken back, they become upset and frustrated. To prevent this situation, clinicians must lead patient relationships and treatment plans. In this chapter, I'll start off by describing clinical leadership and present some questions to help guide your own thinking on the subject. Then, I'll explore a key piece of clinical leadership: having difficult conversations.

Leading Patients

In his book, *The Business of Expertise*, David C. Baker describes the difference between "experts" and "supplicants"—as he calls them [1]. Experts lead client engagements. They determine the appropriate course of action and guide the client through it. Much like healthcare, the role of the clinician is to hear and understand the patient's symptoms, complaints, and experiential perspective; then use their clinical knowledge and understanding to determine the source of the problem and develop a range of treatment options.

Then, acting as a true knowledge translator, the clinician sits down with the patient to discuss the problem and possible solutions. Together the patient and the clinician determine the best course of action, given the unique circumstances. However, one thing should never change: the clinician should guide the conversation.

Contrast that with nonexperts. They *don't* guide the patient or lead the engagement. They are at the mercy of the client's preferences.

We've all had those patients in our clinics. Those patients don't care too much about this exercise or that. They simply want you to do some "massage" (aka manual therapy) and then see them at the next appointment. A true expert clinician manages these patient relationships by establishing themselves as the leader of that clinical engagement and then guiding the patient through the treatment process.

Given the importance of leading patient relationships, it's helpful to assess where you stand. Understanding the way you typically handle patient relationships allows you to make changes as you need.

Self-awareness is a fundamental element of self-improvement and personal/professional development.

Questions to Ask About Leading Patients

As I mentioned earlier, most clinicians will say that they deliver patient-centered and individualized care. They say that they lead the engagement as the expert, licensed clinicians. However, there is a difference between providing patient-centered care and simply acting as an order taker during treatment planning and execution in an effort to be "patient-centered." In fact, as a licensed clinician, it is your professional and ethical responsibility to make sure that you are intentionally guiding and leading your patients through the treatment process.

It helps to reevaluate yourself and your practices to make sure that you're living up to your professional responsibility to direct or lead the patient relationship and plan of care. Here are some questions to ponder and reflect on when evaluating whether there is room for improvement or areas that need to be addressed.

Do You Simply Run Patients Through the Mill, or Do You Take the Time to Learn About Their Unique Situation?

As I've mentioned throughout this book: every patient you see experiences their injury, illness, or dysfunction differently. Patients can't simply be reduced to a diagnosis or set of limitations to be "fixed." Clinicians and clinics that lead their patients understand that there are many factors at play in a patient's specific situation. Biological, physiological, social, physiological, and even environmental factors influence an individual's circumstances. In fact, these factors not only affect their symptoms, progress, and engagement in treatment but also affect satisfaction and retention rates.

Clinicians who lead the patient relationship and engagement take the initiative to understand where each of their patients is coming from. They take the time to understand the unique circumstances and situations that affect their subjective experience of their illness, injury, or dysfunction.

When you take the time to learn those things, you naturally realize that offering "run-of-the-mill" assessment and treatment simply doesn't cut it.

Do You Run Patients Through the Same Exercise or Treatment Program That You Run Most Patients Through, or Do You Create a Treatment Plan That's More Customized and Unique?

It's very easy, especially in outpatient PT settings to fall into a rut, where every patient does the same set of exercises. It makes it easier for you as a clinician too. All you have to do is modify the reps and maybe grade the activity up or down depending on that patient's abilities and tolerance. And in a world where time-based productivity drives many decisions about clinic and caseload management, it's no surprise that this becomes more common.

However, as mentioned in Chapter 7, when productivity and efficiency metrics dominate the environment in the clinic, both patients and clinicians feel the pain. Clinicians burn out trying to hit productivity numbers and running patients through cookie-cutter treatment protocols. Patients lose the human—or person-to-person—experience and service that healthcare should be.

Clinicians who truly aim to deliver patient-centered care need to intentionally work to develop unique and customized treatment plans. There are, of course, some elements of treatment that must remain the same from patient to patient. For example, all patients who undergo a rotator cuff repair will have to comply with the standard postsurgical precautions. Even the early exercises and movements must remain standardized between patients. However, what you can do as the clinician is to allow the patient to prioritize their goals for treatment, and then put together a plan that will help them meet those goals. Allowing your patients to prioritize their goals for treatment improves experience and engagement.

Do You Let Your Patients Tell You What They Want to Do (or What They Want You to Do) During Treatment?

We've all had *that* patient. You know, the one that comes in and says something to the effect of, "Hey, why don't you just put some heat on me and then do some of that *massage* and call it a day?" (First of all, don't get me started on the difference between *massage* and *manual therapy* ....)

How do you handle patients like that?

Many times, you may put up an initial fight to statements like that. Then, after a while—especially on a bad day—you give in. You allow your patient to dictate the plan of care to you. You rely only on what your patients *want* to do (or have done) instead of what you know they *need* to do.

Now, most of the time, clinicians don't intentionally let patients steamroll them. It just tends to be easier. It's easier than having difficult conversations with patients about *why* they should do this exercise or that treatment. It's easier than dealing with patient complaints or—gasp!—negative online reviews.

If you think about the root of this problem, however, it often stems from a *lack* of patient-centered thinking and planning. It stems from not wanting to "deal" with the patient's opinions, feelings, or choices or to have those difficult conversations (more on that in a bit). It's easier to just let them do the exercises they want or provide the manual therapy they're asking for than it is to have a conversation about *why* they do or don't want a certain treatment. It's easier to go along instead of digging down to the root of their complaints, opinions, or choices.

Now, you can, and should, still guide treatment while letting your patients prioritize their goals (as mentioned in the previous section). However, the key is to *guide* (or lead) the patient and their treatment. This requires that you take the time to understand why they are asking for a specific treatment over another.

Once you understand the patient's motivation, you can have a conversation with the patient about it. It may require you to provide some instruction or education, or it may require you to make some modifications to the treatment plan. Oftentimes, a patient's previous experiences may influence their expectations (as mentioned previously in this book). The role of the clinical leader is to address these expectations at the outset of treatment. At the end of the day, it is your responsibility, as the clinician, to take the leadership role.

Do You—as the Clinical Leader—Take the Time to Educate
Your Patient and Then Collaboratively Work to Put Together a
Treatment Plan That Will Help Them Meet Their Goals?

As I just mentioned, part of your role as a clinician is to educate your
patients about their diagnosis or limitations, typical prognosis or expected
outcomes, options for treatment, the effectiveness of those options,
and any risks or precautions associated with them. Part of this involves
answering questions, but it can also include other types of communication and education. The way you answer questions, ask questions, or
seek information from your patients subtly signals to them the type of
information you care about. How you explain and educate your patients
can also impact their clinical outcomes as well as their experience and
engagement in treatment.

After doing the education and finding out some information from
your patients, you can't stop there. You need to use that information to
collaboratively work with your patient to build a treatment plan that will
help them meet their goals.

Your role as the clinician is to provide information about treatment
options and probable outcomes and then work with your patients to
determine which course of action is the best option for *that* patient.

Given the patient's unique circumstances and situation, their goals,
and their dysfunction or diagnoses, what is the best and most effective
treatment option? Once you come up with an answer for that question,
then you guide the patient in selecting specific exercises, interventions, and
modalities to help them meet those goals. Throughout this process, you
take the role of leader or guide. Your patient may ask you which option
you'd recommend. They may need some more information to help inform
their decision.

This process results in a treatment plan that you know has a high likelihood of success and that the patient is more likely to be actively engaged
in. And, at the end of the day, that's what you want.

Summary: Becoming a Clinician–Leader

There's been a consistent thread in all of these questions. And that thread
relates to the human interactions and experiences of both the clinician

and the patient during assessment, treatment planning, and treatment execution. As I am fond of saying: healthcare is a human experience.

Part of that human experience involves social interactions, relationship forming, and role establishment. In order to provide the highest quality of care in a way that leads to engaged and happy patients, you as the clinician must take the leadership role in the relationship. Sometimes, that involves approaching difficult topics around expectations, perceptions, or beliefs about treatment. We discussed the importance of interpersonal skills and communication a few chapters back, but now we'll look at a specific example: difficult conversations.

Leading Your Patients Through Difficult Conversations

Alright, I'm going to come right out and say it: you need to speak your mind!

Patients and clients want it. In fact, they *need* you to be confident enough in your clinical expertise to have hard conversations, push back against unrealistic expectations, and care enough about them and their situation to have that difficult conversation. You need to be able to say what you're thinking in a confident, kind, and caring way.

It seems, for whatever reason, clinicians find it difficult to have "difficult" conversations with patients or clients. Maybe it's because, being in the service field, there's an idea that conflict or confrontation is bad. Since healthcare has begun to move more toward consumer-driven models, some clinicians feel as if they should stand behind the principle: "The customer is always right." There's just one problem with that idea: it doesn't apply in healthcare.

As a licensed clinician, your role is to lead the patient or client engagement. That means that you guide the process of assessment, treatment planning, and goal setting with your patient. It requires that you not sit back passively and let patients continue with decreased engagement, inappropriate or unrealistic expectations, or ideas and behaviors that may actually be making their situation worse.

The Hard Skills

I've written and spoken a lot about the importance of building your interpersonal and communication skills as a clinician in the past but hadn't addressed the issue of "hard" or "difficult" conversations until recently. It came up in a client meeting and I realized that it was a crucial piece of this concept of clinical leadership. As a clinician, your role is to lead the patient engagement, and leadership often means taking the initiative to address difficult topics, mismatched or inappropriate expectations, and even deliver unsettling or "bad" news to patients and their families.

I like saying that the "soft" skills really are the "hard" skills in healthcare. As clinicians and scientifically minded folks, many of us find it easy to acquire information and knowledge and apply it to a patient's or client's situation. For example, it's easy to understand the complex nature of the four components of the shoulder complex, assess a patient who presents to our clinic with shoulder pain, and then develop some treatment plan based solely on the biomechanical or pathophysiological dysfunctions that the patient presents with.

However, clients and patients are more than just joints and tissues. In fact, as I've discussed throughout this book, taking a biopsychosocial (BSP) approach provides a great framework for addressing the *other* factors at play with any patient or client that walks into your clinic.

So, that leaves healthcare practitioners with a situation to deal with: the technical information and skills related to providing healthcare treatment and services aren't the only thing to be mastered. Because patients and clients are unique individuals, with unique and subjective experiences, on a unique road to recovery and healing, clinicians must learn and master interpersonal communication skills to effectively help them reach their goals. This also improves clinical outcomes. In fact, evidence suggests that improving patient–clinician interactions improves population health, provider experience, and even the cost of care [2].

This need to master interpersonal communication skills extends far beyond education, answering questions, and explaining things to your patients. It must extend to the sometimes uncomfortable, sometimes difficult areas of expectations, appropriate recommendations, addressing behavioral change, and the importance of active versus passive treatment.

As a clinician, you should act as a leader and guide, helping your clients achieve their desired goals. This often means that we need to address areas such as harmful lifestyle habits, mismatched expectations about treatment and prognosis, and even the role that they (the client) must play in their own treatment plan. These conversations can be difficult. They can be uncomfortable. But, they are absolutely essential for building rapport, establishing trust, and developing strong, long-lasting relationships with your clients and patients.

Difficult Conversations

When was the last time you had a "difficult" conversation with a patient or client?

What was the topic or issue that led to the conversation?

How did you handle it?

What was the result?

Being a clinician myself and spending much of my clinical work in the VA health system, I've had my fair share of "difficult" conversations with disgruntled patients. Most often than not, much of the anger or frustration expressed by these patients stemmed from differing or unrealistic expectations. I've written and spoken about this a lot over the years, but it bears restating: if you don't address patient expectations at the outset of a course of treatment, you risk the patient becoming dissatisfied, unhappy, disengaged, and possibly even angry with the experience they have in your clinic. Managing patient expectations should be a top priority.

So, how do you go about actually initiating one of these difficult conversations?

What if a patient says something during an assessment or during treatment that leads you to believe they have unrealistic or inappropriate expectations about treatment, and so on?

There are plenty of frameworks out there, from the *Radical Candor* approach to the *Crucial Conversations* guide [3, 4]. Whichever framework or tool you use, the fundamental principles pretty much remain the same. These principles extend not just simply to difficult conversations and topics but also to other areas of communication. Sales, negotiation, and regular, person-to-person conversations, all require similar communication skills.

If you've read many books on communication, whether it be a book about handling confrontation or a book on negotiating, it all boils down to a few basic principles:

- Don't shy away from the difficult topic.
- Employ empathetic, active listening during the conversation.
- Allow the other party to feel heard.
- Provide a context and restate your objection/position/feedback.
- Don't make it personal.

Now that's all good and nice, but it's *how* you do it that really makes the difference, especially when communicating with patients and clients. Let's break down each of those five principles in more detail and discuss how they fit into clinician leadership.

Don't Shy Away

One of the greatest pieces of advice I ever received in my career (and probably life) was that, in order to truly be a successful leader, you must not shy away from doing the hard stuff. In this case, the hard stuff means those difficult conversations.

Humans tend to avoid conflict.

This stems from our evolutionary roots and the fact that societies have formed around the ideas of being nice, not rocking the boat, or going along to get along. And for the most part, those ideas help keep society running smoothly. That's why we can live in a place surrounded by people we don't know, living different lives, and making different choices, and still smile and wave as we walk past each other on the sidewalk. As a rule, most people avoid conflict and try to "go with the flow," in order to avoid any visceral feelings of discomfort, anxiety, or unrest that arise from the conflict.

Now, this tendency to avoid conflict, sometimes at all costs, proves useful in keeping society running smoothly. However, it is actually damaging when it's applied to one-on-one or individual relationships. Unlike interactions out in society, one-on-one interactions and relationships require trust, understanding, and meaningful dialogue.

Translated to the clinical context, where a client or patient is interacting with a clinician, a simple smile and wave aren't enough to establish any meaningful relationship. To build trust, a meaningful exchange or a dialogue must occur. Sometimes, those meaningful dialogues involve clinical decision making. It can be difficult to make decisions about a treatment approach or plan of care when the patient wants something that violates the clinician's clinical experience, the standard of care, or the evidence around effective treatment options [5].

As a clinician, you should establish a leadership role in that relationship. And this is best done by tackling potential stumbling blocks head-on at the beginning. Don't shy away from addressing potential areas of conflict at the outset of treatment.

Allowing incorrect ideas, assumptions, or expectations to linger only increases the difficulty to address them later on in the course of treatment and increases the likelihood of a major conflict or a negative patient experience.

However, as I'll discuss in the coming pages, this requires doing so in a private way, with adequate time to avoid interruptions, clarity, and honesty when discussing the information, and an empathetic, caring attitude [6]. You can't simply barrel into a sensitive topic in an attempt to "set the record straight" or "discuss what will *actually* work." You must approach the topic in a way that builds trust and rapport with the patient.

Trust plays a vital role in healthcare. It makes patients feel less vulnerable. It also makes you, the clinician feel more effective, as increasing trust improves the flow of information between your patients and yourself [7]. And, oftentimes, difficult conversations provide the opportunity for trust to develop between clinicians and patients. When you take the time to address difficult topics with patients, you show them that you care enough about them to risk the relationship by addressing that difficult topic. That, in and of itself, speaks volumes to the patient about where your priorities truly lie.

Employ Empathetic, Active Listening

Now, in order to truly hear and recognize when a potential conflict may arise, you must always practice active listening. Whether you're completing an initial assessment or running through a routine treatment session, you must always attune your ears to hear what a patient is truly saying.

This involves empathy as well—trying to understand the point of view your patient holds—or trying to understand where they're coming from. The literature actually suggests that effective active listening in healthcare includes: being attentive, emotionally involved, and nonjudgmental [8]. This requires, at times, putting down your notes, your computer, or a paper chart (do people still use those?) and focusing on your patient's words. Healthcare can be described as a relational process facilitated by an "engaged and person-centered listener, leading to relational outcomes (e.g., mutual engagement, collaboration) and client-specific outcomes" [8]. That listener is you, the clinician. You are the one charged with leading that patient encounter or engagement in a way that facilitates achieving those desired outcomes.

When you become actively engaged in listening to your patients and clients, you're able to pick up on those "red flags" that need to be addressed. And in order to address them in a way that is collaborative, that builds trust, and that strengthens your relationship with the patient, you must be armed with the information and context that only comes through active listening and empathy. Now, empathy involves more than mere sympathy or even a slight *intuition* about the patient's emotions or thoughts. Rather, real empathy in healthcare involves identification of the patient's feelings and their biological or psychological status [9].

For example, if a patient says something either during treatment or an assessment that makes you feel like there are mismatched or unrealistic expectations, you should not allow that expectation to fester. Now, *how* you address it requires that you've truly heard the patient, understand their point of view, and then frame your objection in a way that reflects that you've listened and understood.

You could say something like, "It seems you have *[insert expectation/idea]* about *[treatment, scheduling, etc.]*. I just want you to know we actually *[insert your objection here]*. How does that sound [or: is that consistent with what you had in mind]?"

This simple exchange establishes that (1) you were listening, (2) you feel there's something that requires further dialogue, and (3) you're open to hearing more about this patient's point of view. Don't worry about bringing forward some criticism of your patient's thought process or beliefs. In fact, research shows that "exaggerated tolerance" toward a patient can generate a form of dishonesty that has a negative effect on the interpersonal relationship [9]. Simply put: if you're truly listening and understanding a patient's perspective, it's only natural that you'll likely have a disagreement or notice an area where your patient has inaccurate assumptions or expectations. Stepping into the discomfort and addressing those areas help to improve your relationship with that patient.

This all falls flat, however, if you don't make the effort to actively listen and understand your patient's understanding or point of view.

Allow the Other Party to Feel Heard

Now, along with empathy and active listening comes the lynchpin: allowing the other party (in this case, your patient) to feel heard. As I've said before, most patients are used to being talked *to* in a healthcare situation, rather than engaging in a dialogue. While patient-centered care is supported in the literature, many healthcare organizations and clinicians still rely on a hierarchical approach to healthcare; one where the clinician is at the top, issuing edicts to the patients below them.

This dynamic ruins the possibility of truly collaborative relationship building between clinicians and patients. The first step to overcoming this is to allow your patients to feel listened to, heard, and valued. To establish a real therapeutic alliance, you as the clinician must already possess a deep understanding of the medical knowledge required to treat that disease or dysfunction, but you must also gather important information from the patient to understand how their context, beliefs, and past experiences are affecting their current situation and experience with this diagnosis [9].

Asking questions like—"Is that consistent with your understanding?"; "Does that sound like what you were thinking?"; or even "Tell me if I'm missing something here."—prompts the patient to provide more information and background to the conversations and also gives them the feeling of being heard. Oftentimes, mistrust in healthcare stems from large differences in each patient's background, knowledge about their own health status, and nonparallel goals of treatment of the clinical team versus those of the patient and their family [7]. Combatting this requires you, the clinician, to work at understanding where your patient is coming from. Only then can you begin to address those gaps in understanding, in an effort to improve your patient's overall understanding of their own health situation.

Ultimately, in any conversation, argument, or negotiation, humans want to be heard, especially in matters that are deeply important and meaningful (like their health, their treatment, and their goals). The research suggests that true professional competence for clinicians becomes apparent through in-depth practical knowledge as well as an ability to creatively apply that knowledge in an individualized manner for each unique patient [9]. This requires the clinician to deeply understand each patient's unique situation in order to tailor treatment to their unique circumstances. Mutual understanding, engagement, relationship-building, and collaboration between clinicians and patients hinge on the trust that comes from a patient truly feeling heard and understood [8].

This leads to a truly person-centered perspective that affects treatment planning and, ultimately, clinical outcomes.

Provide Context and Restate Your Position

After you've provided the opportunity for your patient to clarify their point or provide more background or information, the next step requires that you do the same, if necessary.

Maybe, the patient explains that they have an expectation about treatment that doesn't align with your philosophy of care, or scope of practice, organizational guidelines, or even the clinical evidence. After you've asked those questions that prompt the patient to provide more information for you to truly understand their position, you are then responsible for providing the same type of context and information to the patient. This helps you both understand each other's position and move forward in the relationship from the same understanding.

Now, I can't remember where I first came across this idea, but a good framework that I like to operate from looks something like this:

Restate the other party's position + provide your own context/info + restate (or deliver) your objection or feedback

Let's take the example of a patient who has an unrealistic expectation for treatment. You as the clinician, after asking questions to understand their point of view, may say something like, "It seems that your idea of treatment involves *[insert their expectation]*. In situations like this *[insert context, maybe literature, best practices, organizational standards, etc.]*. And for that reason, *[insert objection and explanation]*."

You can also add a final step of allowing the patient to respond/feel heard (thus beginning the cycle over again) by adding a question like, "How does that sound to you?" or "Is that consistent/compatible with what you're wanting to get out of treatment?"

Your goal with this is to let the patient know you heard and acknowledged their position, provide some background information (if necessary), and then deliver your objection or feedback in a way that leaves the door open for further dialogue and explanation as needed. You don't want it to come across as, "I hear you, but this is what we're going to do instead." Again, the aim is to build strong, collaborative relationships with your patients.

Don't Make It Personal

The final point on this matter involves not taking anything that is said during one of these conversations personally. Oftentimes, especially in matters of health, treatment planning, and the like, emotions run high. A patient may have inappropriate expectations for treatment, but they likely stem from either past experience, incomplete information, or some emotion (fear, anxiety, etc.) about their condition, diagnosis, or limitation. In these situations, patients may say things that, on the surface, seem to be personal attacks on you, your treatment skills, or the like. In all reality, these comments likely stem from an emotional reaction or position related to their current situation.

During these difficult conversations, practice extending the benefit of the doubt, or goodwill, to your patient. They're likely dealing with a situation that's difficult, painful, and even frightening.

What patients need the most is a competent, caring clinician who will take the time to listen to them, acknowledge their feelings, and then provide the necessary context and feedback to begin moving forward toward whatever the desired outcome of treatment is. Adopt an intention to become an "engaged and person-centered listener" who is *with* and *for* your patient [8]. As the clinician, you determine how the relationship develops with the patient.

You can either choose your actions in a way that forms a mutually beneficial relationship for both yourselves and your patients [9], or in a way that leads to communication breakdown and lack of trust. That includes, at times, making the decision to not take anything said in one of these difficult conversations personally. Because, again, your communication with a patient can demonstrate your leadership within the therapeutic context, and it can also act as a therapeutic technique or clinical skill [9].

Your communication with a patient helps build, or detract from, a strong therapeutic relationship which you can leverage, on the behalf of your patient to help them achieve their goals and overcome their limitations. So, don't let something said in a heat-of-the-moment discussion about treatment plans or techniques get in the way of that relationship.

Summary

At the end of the day, clinicians can't hide behind technical skills, book knowledge, or certifications. Healthcare is a relationship-based profession. And relationships, built on trust and collaboration often require times of conflict and resolution.

Learning how to navigate these difficult conversations provides clinicians the ability to ensure that they are able to properly lead their patients throughout a course of treatment to help them achieve their desired outcomes and goals.

Mastering these conversations requires empathy, active listening, deference, and allowing the other party to feel heard. It also requires that clinicians don't shy away from those difficult conversations when they arise. Those clinicians who rise to the challenge find themselves developing strong, long-lasting relationships with their patients; and their patients become more engaged in treatment, achieve better outcomes, and have more positive experiences in the clinic.

CHAPTER 9

Summary

A Higher Standard

My favorite fiction book is *The Alchemist*, by Paulo Coelho. It's a story of a boy who embarks on a great journey to discover his true purpose and uncover a great treasure he has a dream about. In fact, one of my favorite life lesson quotes comes from *The Alchemist*, where the narrator tells the story of a boy who travels to the wisest man in the world to discover the meaning of happiness. The wise man tells him he is busy, but the boy is instructed to look around the marvelous palace while making sure not to spill some oil that is placed in a spoon for him. The boy comes back and the wise man asks the boy what he thinks about the gardens, the palace, and the views. The boy replies that he didn't observe any of that. He was trying not to spill the oil. So, the wise man tells the boy to go back and take all the beauty in. He does just that and returns to the wise man. He tells the wisest of wise men how much he enjoyed the gardens, tapestries, and woodwork in the palace. The wise man then asks the boy what happened to the oil in the spoon. The boy looks down and realizes that he had spilled it all along the way. The wise man responds with this: "The secret of happiness is to see all the marvels of the world, but never forget about the drops of oil on the spoon."

When I first read this, I immediately fell in love with this quote. Especially as healthcare providers, it is easy to get wrapped up in "doing" healthcare.

We complete assessments, write our notes, and implement treatment protocols—all while making sure we're meeting the set productivity and utilization metrics—without really thinking about *why* we're doing any of it.

For us healthcare professionals and clinicians, our patients are the drops of oil in the spoon. So, the way I see it, the key to feeling fulfilled in your work as a healthcare provider is to learn as much as you can, implement new treatment methods, and advance your career, but never forget about the patients you serve every day.

New technology, innovative treatment techniques, operational efficiency, and even things like population health are all good, but they are secondary to the primary purpose of healthcare: helping individual people improve their health and well-being, overcome injuries or dysfunctions, and chart their own path toward healing and long-term recovery. Even when it comes to population health as a whole, the most effective way to make any headway in that regard lies in the ability to affect individual patient lives.

As healthcare professionals, it becomes easy in our day-to-day work to get bogged down in the *process* of delivering healthcare services or managing healthcare programs. We lose sight of the individual, human relationships that are not only a byproduct but a necessary requirement of healthcare service delivery.

As I've written numerous times throughout this book: healthcare is a human experience. It involves one person, skilled in the art of healing, helping, and serving another person who is on their own, unique road to recovery. While lofty goals of improving population or public health through new technologies or service delivery methods are grand and good, it's the individual people and patients, the drops of oil in the spoon, that matter at the end of the day.

A New Healthcare

It's time for a change. It's time that we, as clinicians and healthcare professionals, begin to return our attention back to where it belongs: our patients, their goals and priorities, and their desired outcomes.

For too long, we've allowed third-party payers, administrators, and number-crunchers to dictate how we provide care. Driven by time-based productivity metrics, utilization, treatment units, and fee-for-service payment models that incentivize quantity over quality, clinicians continue to work to the point of burnout, while their patients receive cookie-cutter and run-of-the-mill healthcare treatments and services. Patients, disengaged from treatment, decide that there are other options out there to help them achieve their goals and begin to bounce around from clinic to clinic. Or, sometimes, they simply give up together. They drop off of schedules, cancel appointments, or even "ghost" clinics—never to be heard from again.

It all comes down to this: gone are the days of protocol-based, one-size-fits-most healthcare. We live in a world that is hyper-connected through technology, where everything from car insurance to food products can be had on-demand and in a relatively individualized manner. It's no surprise then that patients today expect healthcare services to be delivered in a timely, efficient, cost-effective, and individualized way. Combine this with the fact that rising deductibles and out-of-pocket costs leave these patients picking up more of the final bill, and you get a recipe for a more consumer-driven healthcare industry.

Patients, now spending more of their own money on services, and empowered by the information-rich environment provided by the Internet and technology, have become more discerning in choosing healthcare providers. They recognize which organizations or individual providers truly care about them, their situation, and their expectations for treatment. They choose to spend their limited time and financial resources on healthcare treatments and services that are more than simply cookie-cutter-based approaches to treatment.

Patients don't want to feel like parts on a conveyor belt or herds of cattle moving through a "process" or "system." Patients want to feel heard, listened to, and understood. They want a more active role in their healthcare decisions, and they look to clinicians and organizations for guidance and help in making those decisions.

In the healthcare of the not-so-distant future, BSP-driven healthcare professionals and organizations will outperform, outlast, and outlive competitors stuck in the old model of healthcare. They'll do this by leveraging clinical expertise, evidence-based resources, and the individualized factors of each patient to improve clinical outcomes, operational efficiency, and patient experience and satisfaction. A byproduct of this shift includes an increase in revenue, and a jump off the productivity-driven, fee-for-service healthcare hamster wheel.

Creating a New Healthcare Paradigm

As I mentioned in the introduction of this book: the shift to a more person-centered, value-based approach to healthcare requires a fundamental change in the way healthcare services are bought, sold, and paid for. It requires an alignment of incentives between the major stakeholders in healthcare: payers, providers, patients, and policy makers.

Now, it should be obvious at this point in the book, but my primary focus lies on the "end user" or the ultimate recipient of the goods or services being bought and sold: the patient. Most of the discussion around the value, efficiency, and effectiveness of healthcare services comes from the point of view of either payers or providers, with some input from policy makers. However, when it comes to defining value or effectiveness in healthcare, we must consider the "for whom" question. And, as far as this book is concerned, the answer is "for the patient."

That being said, in the coming pages, I aim to summarize the eight previous chapters or commitments and tie it all up in a nice bow around this concept of *"what does real value-based healthcare look like?"* from the perspective of the patient.

Ultimately, as healthcare providers, managers, and administrators, we want our organizations to deliver high-impact, high-value services to patients in a way that is feasible, sustainable, and profitable. It serves no one to deliver services that patients may consider truly valuable if it ultimately leads to our organizations going bankrupt, becoming too inefficient, or even ineffective.

As I'll discuss below, value in healthcare is transferred through relationships: the relationship that patients have with a healthcare organization and the relationship that forms between the clinician and the patient. Again, because healthcare is a human experience, it stands to reason that interpersonal relationships and interactions make up a core component of any healthcare encounter or interaction.

The Eight Commitments and Human Relationships

So, how do the eight commitments I've discussed throughout this book tie into this concept of building human relationships in healthcare and leveraging those relationships to deliver high-value, high-impact health-care services?

Let's break down each of the eight commitments and how they lead to the formation of strong, long-lasting relationships with patients through which healthcare professionals deliver high-value, high-impact services and treatments.

Adopting a BSP Approach

This is one of the easiest connections to make. Obviously, taking a BSP approach fundamentally changes the way clinicians view individual patients. No longer is a patient a "rotator cuff patient" for example. The literature suggests that individual, psychological factors have an impact on clinical outcomes of patients with rotator cuff pathology, especially when it comes to postsurgical long-term outcomes [1].

That means two patients, with the exact same diagnosis—in this case, rotator cuff pathology—who receive the same treatment may likely experience differing outcomes. And those outcomes have little to do with the pathophysiological factors at play. Their outcomes differ due to psychological or environmental factors.

So, by taking a BSP approach, requires healthcare professionals to learn more about their patients' unique situations and circumstances. This means they must ask deeper questions, actively listen to the answers, and then use that information to build a more individualized treatment plan. A natural byproduct of asking deeper questions and actively listening to the answers is the development of trust, therapeutic rapport, and a real relationship. The entire healthcare encounter moves deeper than a simple transaction and moves toward true value creation in the form of knowledge transfer and more effective treatments.

This, in turn, ensures that the services (interventions, treatment techniques, delivery methods, etc.) delivered to that patient become more valuable in the long term. Because taking a more individualized approach to treatment means that cookie-cutter treatment plans fall to the wayside, patients experience better clinical and functional outcomes.

Focus on Building Meaningful Relationships

By the nature of this commitment, the relationship piece of the equation gets taken care of. But, how does that translate to higher-value delivery in healthcare?

As I discussed earlier in this book, the value healthcare professionals bring to any patient encounter lies in their knowledge and clinical expertise. It's not about your ability to do something to or for a patient, though you may end up doing so during the course of care. Your value as a healthcare professional lies in your ability to take that vast, often highly technical, understanding and knowledge in your given specialty area and applying that knowledge to the unique circumstances and situation of the patient sitting in front of you.

I tell clients, employees, and students all the time that technical skills or knowledge is the easy part of healthcare. Anyone can read a textbook, research article, or attend a seminar and learn how to master certain treatment techniques and interventions. The hard part of healthcare is taking that knowledge and applying it to the often convoluted or nonsanitized "real-world" patient. Most patients you see in the clinic don't fit the ideal patient described in randomized controlled trials or the case studies from textbooks. People are messy. They have preconceived expectations, past experiences, and complicating factors that make delivering a "standardized" treatment plan difficult.

That means, as clinicians and healthcare professionals, we must not only understand the technical or clinical side of the equation (all of the research, techniques, interventions, etc.), but we must also understand how to apply those interventions or techniques to each unique patient we see. Oftentimes, that requires the mastery of the "soft skills." Interpersonal interactions between clinicians and patients have the ability to improve clinical outcomes and patient satisfaction and even affect healthcare equity [2, 3]. But, all of that starts with the commitment to build meaningful relationships with patients. Once we do that, we are able to leverage our clinical knowledge and expertise, through our relationship with the patient, to become those knowledge translators I wrote about earlier in the book. Knowledge translation, patient empowerment, and clinical advice elevate any treatment technique or intervention from simply one-size-fits-most to be truly individualized and effective.

Putting People Ahead of Policies and Procedures

People often become forgotten in today's healthcare landscape. Patients are often reduced to numbers on a spreadsheet, data points on graphs, or factors in large equations. That means that, when healthcare organizations look to make changes to policies or procedures, often in an attempt to "improve operational (or clinical) efficiency," the impact of those changes on individual patients receives little thought or consideration.

Patients end up feeling corralled like cattle through streamlined processes and procedures which may improve efficiency on paper. These processes and procedures may actually make workflows more convenient for administrative and clinical staff. But, what about the experience they deliver to the patient?

Again, if interpersonal interactions have such a great impact on patient engagement and clinical outcomes, wouldn't it make sense to try and set up the process of care in a way that allows for more personal and individualized interaction?

Since patient-centered care leads to improved health outcomes and decreased healthcare utilization (lower healthcare spending) [4], healthcare organizations should work to develop policies and procedures that don't simply improve efficiency. These policies and procedures should aim to facilitate individualized treatment planning and healthcare service delivery. Look back at Commitment #3 for an example of patient-centered new patient onboarding procedures.

Communicating Value

When I discussed the value in Chapter 4, I focused on the importance of addressing expectations and context to reframe your patients' understanding of the services or treatments they receive in your clinic. This involves answering questions, addressing concerns, and having potentially difficult conversations about priorities, outcomes, and expectations.

Now, by nature of these conversations, you find yourself in a situation where therapeutic rapport, or a relationship, develops between yourself and the patient. This begins at the first appointment, where a patient's expectations (and therefore value perception) change, either for the better or for the worse [5]. In order to ensure that change is positive, you must seek to understand the patient's current understanding and expectations. This means you need to do all those things we've talked about in this book: active listening, asking the right questions, answering questions, and seeking to truly understand that patient's unique circumstances. Doing those things results in the formation of a real relationship between you and your organization and that patient. You want that patient to walk away from that first encounter with your organization and think "those people really cared about me."

And, if you've truly taken the time to understand that patient and their unique situation, then you're in a position to develop a person-centered, or individualized, treatment plan. You're also able to act as that healthcare guide to your patient. You become more than a "Mr. Fixit." You become the person they rely on for support, understanding, and guidance when it comes to their healthcare or condition.

I remember when I was leaving the VA to start my consulting work. During my last week in that clinic, I had an experience that highlighted this concept of relationship building and delivering high-value services to patients and the impact that it can have. I was in between patients, typing up notes and working on documentation. My back was facing the office door and I heard a knock. I turned around and it was a patient who I hadn't seen in a while. He said, "Hey, I heard you're leaving this place." I told him that it was my last week and that there was an opportunity I couldn't pass up.

He paused and then said, "I don't know if you know this, but when you started seeing me last year, I was in a rough place. I had almost given up on getting care here because I didn't feel like anyone really cared. Then I came to this clinic and you asked me questions about my expectations and priorities. Heck, we even bumped heads a bit. But I knew that you weren't just running me through the mill. You really cared about me, and that meant a lot. Thanks."

I was totally blown away. I hadn't seen this patient in almost a year. And to be honest, I couldn't entirely remember for what diagnosis or condition he was referred. But simply taking the time to understand his expectations for treatment, addressing his priorities, and building a treatment plan around those factors made a huge impression on him. That story shows how simply communicating and addressing value perception in the clinic can lead to the formation of real, long-lasting relationships between clinicians and patients.

Prioritizing Patient Engagement

Patient engagement has been associated with decreased and fewer adverse healthcare events, improved patient self-management of chronic conditions, less diagnostic testing, decreased use of healthcare services, and even shorter lengths of stay in hospitals [4]. Those reasons alone should be enough to make you see and understand the importance of patient engagement.

Again, if high-value, high-impact services involve individualizing care plans and treatment programs, then you must focus on ensuring that you develop treatment plans and programs that patients will actually follow and participate in. That means you should work to understand their unique perspective and context. As mentioned numerous times in this book, the byproduct of that process is the development of trust and relationships.

As mentioned earlier, patient engagement hinges not so much on the technical knowledge or skills of the clinician or healthcare professionals. It hinges on the "soft skills" of those professionals. Interpersonal communication, empathy, and understanding drive a patient's perception of the value of the services they're receiving as well as their willingness to become participants in their care, rather than simply passive recipients.

Embracing Transparency

There are very few areas in normal life that are as confusing, opaque, and obscure as healthcare. Not only are patients at a disadvantage from a knowledge or understanding perspective, but they also lack the ability to easily obtain information related to the costs of receiving care.

This leaves patients in a vulnerable position when they seek out care. They often don't possess the same level of knowledge or understanding about their diagnosis, prognosis, and available treatment options as the providers and clinicians they interact with. That means they enter into the relationship feeling at a disadvantage. They may even feel on guard or defensive. After all, they know what they are feeling and how it affects their daily life, but how can they raise concerns or objections to the professionals who have advanced degrees and years of clinical experience?

Clear, simple communication throughout the treatment process addresses this issue. And, it does so in a way that establishes trust and helps to build that relationship I keep talking about. How clinicians answer questions and educate patients has a huge impact on their overall engagement throughout their treatment plan, their trust and confidence in the treatment itself, and even clinical outcomes in the long term.

The key to delivering truly patient-centered care is you must implement those people-first principles I discussed in that chapter on transparency. Again, patients shouldn't be an afterthought in the process. They're the whole reason the process exists in the first place.

Forgetting Time-Based Productivity and Fee-For-Service Models

I feel as though this commitment changes by necessity when the others become standard practice. We see it happening already, with various third-party payers and policy makers calling for and implementing value-based reimbursement arrangements in healthcare. In reality, much of our infatuation with time-based productivity metrics and KPIs stems from this environment of fee-for-service billing and reimbursement in healthcare. And, as previously discussed, those arrangements fail to represent the true value of a clinician's performance [6].

As we enter into this new world of "value-based" healthcare, clinicians and organizations must give up the line of thinking that sees productivity or value creation as a function of time. Instead, we need to focus on the *outcome* or quality of the healthcare services we deliver.

Obviously, this topic in and of itself could be its own book. I think the main takeaways I would want you to walk away with are: (1) when discussing value in healthcare, we need to clearly define the "value to whom?" piece, (2) we must ensure that patients (the end recipient of the services in question) have a seat at the table in those value discussions, and (3) any system that aims to replace fee-for-service models must ensure that it aligns the incentives of as many stakeholders as possible, with the priority being on person-centered, or individualized treatment planning and service delivery.

Leading Patients

If the value we as healthcare professionals bring to the table is our clinical expertise and knowledge, then we have an obligation—if not a moral imperative—to ensure that we approach each patient encounter with the understanding that we must lead. We act as guides in this process, applying our specialized skill and knowledge to a patient's specific and unique situation in order to help them achieve their desired outcomes or goals. This usually involves some form of healing, recovery, or improvement of their quality of life.

Whatever the desired outcome of a plan of care, one thing is certain: the patient gains nothing when clinicians take a passive approach to treatment. Patients benefit the most when the clinician takes the active leadership role in that encounter. While employing empathy, active listening, deference, and allowing the patient to feel heard, the clinician then applies their clinical skill and knowledge to cocreate a treatment plan with the patient that aims to help them achieve their desired outcomes or goals.

Sometimes, this requires having difficult conversations with patients about expectations or priorities. While you may be tempted to shy away from those potential conflicts, a true clinical leader steps up and addresses areas like harmful lifestyle habits, mismatched expectations for treatment, and even the role that they (the patient) must play in their own treatment plan. Though these conversations may be uncomfortable, and even difficult, they also lead to the development of those long-lasting relationships that I've mentioned so many times throughout this book.

Practical Steps to Take in the Clinic

So, what are some practical steps that you can take in your clinic, organization, or even daily clinical practice to begin shifting the focus of healthcare back toward people?

Well, I feel like I've laid out a bunch of practical strategies throughout this book, but I'll try to summarize a few main points here.

Change From Time-Based Productivity Measures and Metrics to Value-Based or Quality-Based Measures

Now, this one may be easier said than done, and I understand that. However, I firmly believe that the healthcare of tomorrow, if we truly aim to create a system that delivers person-centered, high-value services, must leave behind this notion of fee-for-service or high-volume healthcare.

Because of the way reimbursement and payment are handled in the United States, healthcare organizations and clinics focus on time-based productivity metrics. Clinicians and organizations get paid for the *time* they spend with patients, rather than being paid for the treatment itself, or the outcome of that treatment. This leads to patients receiving more treatment than necessary, and clinicians becoming incentivized to work more slowly to deliver minimally acceptable quality.

By focusing on measuring the value, outcomes, or effectiveness of treatment—and using that to determine payment—healthcare organizations will be incentivized to deliver the most appropriate and effective treatment in the most efficient manner. This is already starting to happen, with Medicare moving toward MIPS and other payers moving toward lump-sum or global service fees.

Now, while individual clinicians or organizations may not have much control over how they get paid for services, they can control the metrics that they track to evaluate performance and quality. As mentioned earlier in this book, quality measures and patient-driven outcome measures offer a great option for gauging not simply how much volume a clinician, department, or organization generates, but the *value* or *quality* of the services being delivered.

Obviously, we need to make sure that we're running organizations or departments that are financially sustainable, so need to track some metrics such as revenue-per-visit and visits-per-day. However, with value-based healthcare on the horizon, implementing and incorporating these value-based measures positions our organizations to thrive in the new age of value-based care, as opposed to struggling and suffering in an attempt to hold onto high-volume healthcare service delivery once the winds of change arrive.

Use Technology to Augment or Improve Human Connection Rather Than Using It Simply for Efficiency

When I was leading an outpatient rehab clinic at a VA hospital, management decided that they would implement a kiosk system in each clinic. Veterans in the waiting area could use the kiosk to schedule/cancel appointments, update contact info, see/pay any outstanding balances, and check-in to their appointments.

On the surface, this sounded like a great idea. However, when it came time to implement the program, management also decided that the kiosks would replace clerical staff in these clinics. They took a useful and effective technology, and made it impersonal, confusing to operate, and largely ineffective during actual use. They could have made the program much more successful by providing the kiosks and using them to augment the user's experience. A veteran could have walked into the clinic, and a friendly clerk or receptionist could have helped the veteran check-in to the appointment and then be there to provide any assistance working or navigating the kiosk menus.

Instead, veterans were met with no human contact, and a machine that they didn't know how to use to check-in to their appointment. So, when implementing technology in healthcare delivery, we need to always keep in mind the human experience that will be on the other end of that technology.

The important thing to remember here is that technology is here to stay. Artificial Intelligence (AI), virtual service delivery, and electronic communication greatly expand the reach and capabilities of healthcare providers. However, you must remember that the true value you bring to the table as a clinician or healthcare professional lies in your ability to deliver those high-impact services and treatments that stem from the relationships you form with patients. By all means, implement new technologies and tools, but never forget that so much of the value in healthcare lies in those true, long-lasting relationships that can be used to support and guide your patients as they make behavioral changes, implement self-management strategies, and ultimately, take the driver's seat in their own health and well-being.

Design the Process of Care to Allow Human Connection and Relationship

Without trying to sound like a broken record: healthcare is about people—patients and providers. It's about a human person skilled in delivering treatment, and serving and healing another person, who is on a unique journey to recovery.

So, how do you take this into account when designing the process of care?

By focusing on the patient and the patient's experience/outcomes rather than financial numbers and metrics. This may be as simple as allowing clinicians extra administrative time to spend reviewing medical records or even something as simple (and less costly) as training receptionists and office staff on how to make the most out of a patient phone call.

Are we simply using a phone call to gather the data necessary to check the boxes on an assessment form, or are we using that call as an opportunity to hear/listen to that patient's story?

Are we using that call to let the patient know that we care about them as an individual and not just how much their insurance company will pay?

How we gather data is arguably as important—if not more important—than the data we actually gather on these phone calls.

Convince and Show Staff/Clinicians That Their Jobs Are Part of the Higher Purpose of the Organization

People want to be part of something greater than themselves. We want to feel that the work we do means something. No clinician I know wakes up and thinks, "I'm ready to go to the clinic and get three billable units out of each patient I see today!" Clinicians want to make real, lasting impacts on the patients they see each day.

So, how do we do that?

By showing them that the organization they're a part of—the team they belong to—works toward some higher calling or higher purpose rather than simply "delivering quality healthcare services."

I'm going to use an example from the physical medicine and rehabilitation world, since that's where I come from. As an example of this, craft some higher purpose statement for your healthcare clinic or organization to the effect of: "We help people with chronic back pain overcome disability and live the life they want." Compare that with the often unsaid, but implied, "You work as a therapist in a back-pain clinic." Do you see how the first statement lays out the goal and vision for why you're showing up for work every day?

Now, this is very much a change that must come from the executive leadership team of that clinic or organization. If the CEO is on a mission to help people live the life they want, that filters its way down to the frontline staff and clinicians.

Organizational leaders should make it their priority not only to effectively communicate the organization's higher purpose but also to make leadership decisions that prioritize it.

Change Your Messaging and Marketing so Your Clients and Prospective Clients Understand and Buy-In to Your Organization's Higher Purpose

This improves patient engagement, experience, and even clinical outcomes.

As with the aforementioned example, this starts with the executive leadership of the organization. Patients who know and understand an organization's higher purpose will buy-in to treatment, become more active participants, and potentially achieve greater outcomes than patients who are simply going to PT twice a week and doing exercises for their shoulder, as an example.

Individual clinicians, organizations, and leaders should spend time focusing on the people they serve and the higher purpose of their organization. Then, keeping those two things in mind, they need to make decisions that reflect that purpose and improve care for those patients.

As mentioned earlier in this book, this could be something as simple as changing the way phone calls are handled at the front desk all the way to changing the actual process of care. The important thing to keep in mind is that, as healthcare providers, we are in this field for more than money. We are in the field to serve people, so we need to make sure our personal and organizational decisions reflect that.

As an individual clinician, this would mean not sacrificing that conviction during the daily routine of treating patients. For patients, this would mean only going to clinics and providers that treat you like a person and not a number. For leaders and executives, this would mean making changes to processes and strategies that focus on delivering real, human care that prioritizes people and relationships over profit.

Summary

Hopefully, if you've stuck with me to this point in the book, you feel encouraged and empowered to make real and significant changes to your clinical practice, organizational processes, or even procedures and policies in your department or facility that return the focus of healthcare back to where it truly belongs: people—the people who receive care and the people who work to deliver that care should be the fundamental focus. Because, again, healthcare is a human experience. It's more than just numbers, spreadsheets, workflows, and processes.

My hope is that this book prompts many discussions about the nature of healthcare. Maybe, it's only an internal discussion in your head about how you approach clinical practice or patient care. Maybe, it prompts more of a widespread discussion between you and your organizational team that ends up affecting real change in the process of care at your facility. Whatever the case, I'm sure you'll agree with me that something needs to change in our current healthcare environment. We can't simply sit back and allow the dehumanization that currently runs rampant in our clinics and hospitals to continue to wreak havoc on one of the most important factors in clinical outcomes: interpersonal interactions and relationships between healthcare professionals and the people (patients) that they serve. Healthcare is a great and noble profession, but it will only remain so if we, as healthcare professionals, return its focus to its true purpose: people, the people receiving care, and the people working to deliver that care. After all, we're all more than simply numbers on spreadsheets or items on checklists.

References

Introduction

[1] Jack, K., S.M. McLean, J.K. Moffett, and E. Gardiner. 2010. "Barriers to Treatment Adherence in Physiotherapy Outpatient Clinics: A Systematic Review." *Manual therapy* 15, no. 3, pp. 220–228. doi:10.1016/j.math.2009.12.004

[2] Bogle, J.C. 2008. *Enough: True Measures of Money, Business, and Life*, p. 125. John Wiley & Sons.

Chapter 1

[1] Borrell-Carrio, F. 2004. "The Biopsychosocial Model 25 Years Later: Principles, Practice, and Scientific Inquiry." *The Annals of Family Medicine* 2, no. 6, pp. 576–582. doi:10.1370/afm.245

[2] Covic, T. 2003. "A Biopsychosocial Model of Pain and Depression in Rheumatoid Arthritis: A 12-Month longitudinal Study." *Rheumatology* 42, no. 11, pp. 1287–1294. doi:10.1093/rheumatology/keg3

[3] Moseley, L. 2002. "Combined Physiotherapy and Education is Efficacious for Chronic Low Back Pain." *Australian Journal of Physiotherapy* 48, no. 4, pp. 297–302. doi:10.1016/s0004-9514(14)60169-0

[4] de Filippis, L.G., S. Gulli, A. Caliri , G. D'Avola, R. Lo Gullo, S. Morgante, C. Romano, F. Munao, G. Trimarchi, D. La Torre, and C. Fichera. 2004. "Factors Influencing Pain, Physical Function and Social Functioning in Patients With Osteoarthritis in Southern Italy." *Int J Clin Pharmacol Res* 24, no. 4, pp. 103–109. Available at: www.ncbi.nlm.nih.gov/pubmed/15754914

[5] Moseley, G.L., and D.S. Butler. 2015. "Fifteen Years of Explaining Pain: The Past, Present, and Future." *The Journal of Pain* 16, no. 9, pp. 807–813. doi:10.1016/j.jpain.2015.05.005

[6] Engel, G.L. 1978. "The Biopsychosocial Model and the Education of Health Professionals?." *Annals of the New York Academy of Sciences* 310(1 Primary Health), pp. 169–181. doi:10.1111/j.1749-6632.1978.tb22070.x

[7] Moseley, G. 2004. "Evidence for a Direct Relationship Between Cognitive and Physical Change During an Education Intervention in People With Chronic Low Back Pain." *European Journal of Pain* 8, no. 1, pp. 39–45. doi:10.1016/s1090-3801(03)00063-6

[8] Louw, A., I. Diener, D.S. Butler, and E.J. Puentedura. 2011. "The Effect of Neuroscience Education on Pain, Disability, Anxiety, and Stress in Chronic Musculoskeletal Pain." *Archives of Physical Medicine and Rehabilitation* 92, no. 12, pp. 2041–2056. doi: https://doi.org/10.1016/j.apmr.2011.07.198

[9] Turk, D.C., and R.J. Gatchel. 2018. "Psychological Approaches to Pain Management: A Practitioners Handbook." New York, NY: The Guilford Press.

[10] Gatchel, R.J., and K.J. Howard. (n.d.). *The Biopsychosocial Approach.* Retrieved from www.practicalpainmanagement.com/treatments/psychological/biopsychosocial-approach

[11] Vetter, T.R., G. McGwin, C.L. Bridgewater, A. Madan-Swain, and L.I. Ascherman. 2013. "Validation and Clinical Application of a Biopsychosocial Model of Pain Intensity and Functional Disability in Patients with a Pediatric Chronic Pain Condition Referred to a Subspecialty Clinic." Pain Research and Treatment, 2013:143292. doi:10.1155/2013/143292

Chapter 2

[1] Kelley, J.M., G. Kraft-Todd, L. Schapira, J. Kossowsky, and H. Riess. 2014. "The Influence of the Patient-Clinician Relationship on Healthcare Outcomes: A Systematic Review and Meta-Analysis of Randomized Controlled Trials." *PloS one* 9, no. 4, p. e94207. doi:10.1371/journal.pone.0094207

[2] Cosio, D., and E. Lin. 2018. "Role of Active Versus Passive Complementary and Integrative Health Approaches in Pain Management." *Global advances in health and medicine* 7, 2164956118768492. https://doi.org/10.1177/2164956118768492

[3] Caneiro, J.P., E.M. Roos, C.J. Barton, K. O'Sullivan, P. Kent, I. Lin, P. Choong, K.M. Crossley, J. Hartvigsen, A.J. Smith, and P. O'Sullivan. 2020. "It Is Time to Move Beyond 'Body Region Silos' to Manage Musculoskeletal Pain: Five Actions to Change Clinical Practice." *Br J Sports Med* 54, no. 8, pp. 438–439. doi:10.1136/bjsports-2018-100488

Chapter 3

[1] Geng, X., Z. Chen, W. Lam, and Q. Zheng. 2013. "Hedonic Evaluation Over Short and Long Retention Intervals: The Mechanism of the Peak-End Rule." *Journal of Behavioral Decision Making* 26, no. 3, pp. 225–236. doi:10.1002/bdm.1755

[2] Happiness: It's All About the Ending. n.d. Retrieved from www.psychologytoday.com/us/blog/fulfillment-any-age/201209/happiness-it-s-all-about-the-ending

Chapter 4

[1] Weingarten, G. April 08, 2007. "Pearls Before Breakfast: Can One of the Nation's Great Musicians Cut Through the Fog of a D.C. Rush Hour? Let's Find Out." Retrieved February 15, 2021, www.washingtonpost .com/lifestyle/magazine/pearls-before-breakfast-can-one-of-the-nations-great-musicians-cut-through-the-fog-of-a-dc-rush-hour-lets-find-out/2014/09/23/8a6d46da-4331-11e4-b47c-f5889e061e5f_story.html

[2] Sterzer, P., C. Frith, and P. Petrovic. 2010. "Believing Is Seeing: Expectations Alter Visual Awareness." *Current Biology* 20, no. 21, p. 1973. doi: 10.1016/j .cub.2010.10.036

[3] Adelson, E.H. 1995. http://persci.mit.edu/gallery/checkershadow

[4] Schwarz, K.A., R. Pfister, and C. Büchel. 2016. "Rethinking Explicit Expectations: Connecting Placebos, Social Cognition, and Contextual Perception." *Trends in Cognitive Sciences* 20, no. 6, pp. 469–480. doi: 10.1016/j.tics.2016.04.001

[5] Berhane, A., and F. Enquselassie. 2016. "Patient Expectations and Their Satisfaction in the Context of Public Hospitals." *Patient preference and adherence* 10, pp. 1919–1928. doi:10.2147/PPA.S109982

[6] Bowling, A., G. Rowe, N. Lambert, M. Waddington, K. Mahtani, C. Kenten, C., A. Howe, and S. Francis. 2012. "The Measurement of Patients' Expectations for Health Care: A Review and Psychometric Testing of a Measure of Patients' Expectations." *Health Technology Assessment* 16, no. 30. doi: 10.3310/hta16300

[7] Rao, J.K. 2000. "Visit-Specific Expectations and Patient-Centered Outcomes: A Literature Review." *Archives of Family Medicine* 9, no. 10, pp. 1148–1155. doi: 10.1001/archfami.9.10.1148

[8] Patient Engagement: Technical Series on Safer Primary Care. 2016. Geneva: World Health Organization. License: CC BY-NC-SA 3.0 IGO. https:// apps.who.int/iris/bitstream/handle/10665/252269/9789241511629-eng .pdf;jsessionid=C3F624201D3DFD55320ABABBD84B58A3?sequence=1

[9] Salazar, R. November 05, 2019. "2019 Survey Results: Outpatient PT & OT Clinicians & Clinic Owners." Retrieved February 15, 2021, https:// rehabupracticesolutions.com/2019-survey/

[10] The Better Outcomes Show. n.d. 006: A Different Way to Approach Chronic Pain. https://rehabupracticesolutions.com/better-outcomes-006/

Chapter 5

[1] Jack, K., S.M. McLean, J.K. Moffett, and E. Gardiner. 2010. "Barriers to Treatment Adherence in Physiotherapy Outpatient Clinics: A Systematic Review." *Manual therapy* 15, no. 3, pp. 220–228. doi:10.1016/j.math.2009 .12.004

[2] What's the Cost of Physical Therapy Without Insurance? https://guidedoc .com/cost-of-physical-therapy-without-insurance

[3] Customer Acquisition Versus Retention. www.sailthru.com/marketing-blog/ written-customer-acquisition-vs-retention-infographic/

[4] Strive Labs. July 17, 2016. *The Physical Therapist's Guide to Patient Retention.* http://cpaprivatepractice.ca/the-physical-therapists-guide-to-patient-retention/

[5] Herbert, S. November 24, 2014. *The Importance of Patient Retention.* WebPT. www.webpt.com/blog/post/importance-of-patient-retention

[6] Hush, J.M., K. Cameron, and M. Mackey. 2011. "Patient Satisfaction With Musculoskeletal Physical Therapy Care: A Systematic Review." *Physical Therapy* 91, no. 1, pp. 25–36. doi:10.2522/ptj.20100061

[7] O'Keefe, M., P. Cullinane, J. Hurley, I. Leahy, and S. Bunzli. 2016. "What Influences Patient-Therapist Interactions in Musculoskeletal Physical Therapy? Qualitative Systematic Review and Meta-Synthesis." *Physical Therapy* 12, no. 04, pp. 163–165. doi:10.1055/s-0035-1567123

[8] CARE Mercer, S.W. Scottish Executive. 2004. The CARE Measure was originally developed by Dr. Stewart Mercer and colleagues as part of a Health Service Research Fellowship funded by the Chief Scientist Office of the Scottish Executive (2000–2003).

Chapter 6

[1] Mondloch, M.V., D.C. Cole, and J.W. Frank. 2001. "Does How You Do Depend on How You Think You'll Do? A Systematic Review of the Evidence for a Relation Between Patients' Recovery Expectations and Health Outcomes. *CMAJ* 165, no. 2, pp. 174–179. Retrieved from www.cmaj.ca/content/ 165/2/174.short

[2] Street, R.L., G. Makoul, N.K. Arora, and R.M. Epstein. 2009. "How Does Communication Heal? Pathways Linking Clinician–Patient Communication to Health Outcomes." *Patient Education and Counseling* 74, no. 3, pp. 295–301. doi:10.1016/j.pec.2008.11.015

[3] Darlow, B., S. Dean, M. Perry, F. Mathieson, G.D. Baxter, and A. Dowell. 2015. "Easy to Harm, Hard to Heal." *Spine* 40, no. 11, pp. 842–850. doi:10.1097/brs.0000000000000901

[4] Darlow, B., A. Dowell, G.D. Baxter, F. Mathieson, M. Perry, and S. Dean. 2013. "The Enduring Impact of What Clinicians Say to People With Low Back Pain." *The Annals of Family Medicine* 11, no. 6, pp. 527–534. doi:10.1370/afm.1518

[5] Gaynor, M., R. Moreno-Serra, and C. Propper. 2010. "Death by Market Power: Reform, Competition and Patient Outcomes in the National Health Service." doi:10.3386/w16164

[6] McKain, S. 2013. *Create Distinction: What to Do When "Great" Isn't Good Enough to Grow Your Business*. Austin, TX: Greenleaf Book Group.

[7] Torpie, K. 2014. "Customer Service vs. Patient Care." *Patient Experience Journal* Vol. 1: Iss. 2, Article 3. Available at: http://pxjournal.org/journal/vol1/iss2/3

[8] Levine, R., K. Shore, J. Lubalin, S. Garfinkel, M. Hurtado, and K. Carman. 2012. "Comparing Physician and Patient Perceptions of Quality in Ambulatory Care." *International Journal for Quality in Health Care* 24, no. 4, pp. 348–356. doi:10.1093/intqhc/mzs023

[9] Diener, I., M. Kargela, and A. Louw. 2016. "Listening Is Therapy: Patient Interviewing From a Pain Science Perspective." *Physiotherapy Theory and Practice* 32, no. 5, pp. 356–367. doi:10.1080/09593985.2016.1194648

[10] Szumigalski, K. 2019. "Why We Need Price Transparency in Healthcare." *Harvard Public Health Review* 22, pp. 1–4. www.jstor.org/stable/48539153

[11] Thaler, R., and C. Sunstein. 2009. *Nudge: Improving Decisions About Health, Wealth, and Happiness: Rev. and Exp. Ed.* Penguin.

[12] "Surprise billing & protecting consumers." n.d. Centers for Medicare & Medicaid Services. www.cms.gov/nosurprises/Ending-Surprise-Medical-Bills

[13] Tiedje, K., N.D. Shippee, A.M. Johnson, P.M. Flynn, D.M. Finnie, J.T. Liesinger, C.R. May, M.E. Olson, J.L. Ridgeway, N.D. Shah, B.P. Yawn, and V.M. Montori. 2013. "'They Leave at Least Believing They Had a Part in the Discussion': Understanding Decision Aid Use and Patient-Clinician Decision-Making Through Qualitative Research." *Patient education and counseling* 93, no. 1, pp. 86–94. https://doi.org/10.1016/j.pec.2013.03.013

[14] Moulton, B., and J.S. King. 2010. "Aligning Ethics With Medical Decision-Making: the Quest for Informed Patient Choice." *J Law Med Ethics* 38, pp. 85–97.

Chapter 7

[1] CARE Mercer, S.W., Scottish Executive. 2004. "The CARE Measure was Originally Developed by Dr. Stewart Mercer and Colleagues as Part of a Health Service Research Fellowship Funded by the Chief Scientist Office of the Scottish Executive (2000–2003)."

[2] PSFS developed by: Stratford, P., C. Gill, M. Westaway, and J. Binkley. 1995. "Assessing Disability and Change on Individual Patients: A Report of a Patient Specific Measure." *Physiotherapy Canada* 47, pp. 258–263.

[3] Merriam-Webster. n.d. *Productivity definition & meaning*. Merriam-Webster. Retrieved February 11, 2022, from www.merriam-webster.com/dictionary/productivity

[4] Rohn, J. (Writer). n.d. The Ultimate Jim Rohn Library.

[5] From the House of Delegates: Help in Responding to 'Productivity' Issues on Its Way. PT in Motion News. July 14, 2014. www.apta.org/PTinMotion/NewsNow/2014/7/9/HoDProductivity/

[6] "Position Statement on Value Versus Productivity Measurement in Acute Care Physical Therapy." *Acute Care.* http://c.ymcdn.com/sites/acutept.site-ym.com/resource/resmgr/Files/2014-11_Productivity_Value_B.pdf

[7] Draper D.O. 2010. "Ultrasound and Joint Mobilizations for Achieving Normal Wrist Range of Motion After Injury or Surgery: A Case Series." *Journal of athletic training* 45, no. 5, pp. 486–491. www.ncbi.nlm.nih.gov/pmc/articles/PMC2938322/

[8] Solid C.A. 2022. "Current Methods of Value Assessments." In: *Practical Strategies to Assess Value in Health Care.* Springer, Cham. https://doi.org/10.1007/978-3-030-95149-8_6

[9] Wells, G.A. 2009. "Patient-Driven Outcomes in Rheumatoid Arthritis." *The Journal of Rheumatology Supplement* 82, no. 0, pp. 33–38. doi:10.3899/jrheum.090129

[10] Potter, P. September 12, 2016. "Are Cash Therapy Practices Good For Patients?" [Web log post]. Retrieved March 20, 2019, www.evidenceinmotion.com/blog/2016/09/12/are-cash-therapy-practices-good-for-patients/

[11] Pulford, K., B. Kilduff, W.J. Hanney, M. Kolber, X. Liu, and R. Miller. 2019. "Service Utilization and Costs of Patients at a Cash-Based Physical Therapy Clinic." *The Health Care Manager* 38, no. 1, pp. 37–43. doi:10.1097/hcm.0000000000000247

Chapter 8

[1] Baker, D.C. 2017. *The Business of Expertise: How Entrepreneurial Experts Convert Insight to Impact + Wealth.* RockBench Publishing.

[2] Drossman, D.A., L. Chang, J.K. Deutsch, A.C. Ford, A. Halpert, K. Kroenke, S. Nurko, J. Ruddy, J. Snyder, and A. Sperber. November 2021. "A Review of the Evidence and Recommendations on Communication Skills and the Patient-Provider Relationship: A Rome Foundation Working Team Report." *Gastroenterology* 161, no. 5, pp. 1670–1688.e7. doi: 10.1053/j.gastro.2021.07.037. Epub July 28, 2021. PMID: 34331912.

[3] Scott, K.M. 2019. *Radical Candor: Be a Kick-Ass Boss Without Losing Your Humanity.* St. Martin's Press.

[4] Grenny, J. 2012. *Crucial Conversations.* McGraw Hill.

[5] Diamond-Brown, L. May 2018. "'It Can Be Challenging, It Can Be Scary, It Can Be Gratifying': Obstetricians' Narratives of Negotiating Patient Choice, Clinical Experience, and Standards of Care in Decision-Making." *Soc Sci*

Med 205, pp. 48–54. doi: 10.1016/j.socscimed.2018.04.002. Epub April 05, 2018. PMID: 29635190.

[6] Collini, A, H. Parker, and A. Oliver. February 2021. "Training for Difficult Conversations and Breaking Bad News Over the Phone in the Emergency Department." *Emerg Med J* 38, no. 2, pp. 151–154. doi: 10.1136/emermed-2020-210141. Epub December 03, 2020. PMID: 33273038.

[7] Lee, T.H., E.A. McGlynn, and D.G. Safran. 2019. "A Framework for Increasing Trust Between Patients and the Organizations That Care for Them." *JAMA* 321, no. 6, pp. 539–540. doi:10.1001/jama.2018.19186

[8] King, G. October 2021. "Central Yet Overlooked: Engaged and Person-Centred Listening in Rehabilitation and Healthcare Conversations." *Disabil Rehabil* 14, pp. 1–13. doi: 10.1080/09638288.2021.1982026. Epub ahead of print. PMID: 34647516.

[9] Chichirez, C.M., and V.L. Purcărea. 2018. "Interpersonal Communication in Healthcare." *Journal of medicine and life* 11, no. 2, pp. 119–122.

Chapter 9

[1] Sheikhzadeh, A., M.M. Wertli, S.S. Weiner, E. Rasmussen-Barr, and S. Weiser. 2021. "Do Psychological Factors Affect Outcomes in Musculoskeletal Shoulder Disorders? A Systematic Review." *BMC Musculoskelet Disord* 22, p. 560. https://doi.org/10.1186/s12891-021-04359-6

[2] Peimani, M., G. Garmaroudi, A.L. Stewart, M. Yekaninejad, E. Shakibazadeh, and E. Nasli-Esfahani. July 2021. "Patient-Physician Interpersonal Processes of Care at the Time of Diabetes Treatment Intensification and Their Links to Patient Outcomes." *Patient Educ Couns* 104, no. 7, pp. 1659–1667. doi: 10.1016/j.pec.2020.12.008. Epub December 25, 2020. PMID: 33431242.

[3] Bridges, C., D.M. Duenas, H. Lewis, K. Anderson, D.J. Opel, B.S. Wilfond, and S.A. Kraft. 2021. "Patient Perspectives on How to Demonstrate Respect: Implications for Clinicians and Healthcare Organizations." *PLoS ONE* 16, no. 4, p. e0250999. https://doi.org/10.1371/journal.pone.0250999

[4] Herrin, J., K.G. Harris, K. Kenward, S. Hines, M.S. Joshi, and D.L. Frosch. 2016. "Patient and Family Engagement: A Survey of US Hospital Practices." *BMJ Quality & Safety* 25, pp. 182–189.

[5] Berhane, A., and F. Enquselassie. 2016. "Patient Expectations and Their Satisfaction in the Context of Public Hospitals." *Patient preference and adherence* 10, pp. 1919–1928. doi:10.2147/PPA.S109982

[6] From the House of Delegates: Help in Responding to 'Productivity' Issues on Its Way. PT in Motion News. July 14, 2014. www.apta.org/PTinMotion/NewsNow/2014/7/9/HoDProductivity/

About the Author

Rafael E. Salazar II, MHS, OTR/L (Rafi) is the principal owner of Rehab U Practice Solutions, a leader in patient retention strategy. He has worked in a variety of rehab settings, treating patients recovering from a variety of injuries and surgeries. He worked as the lead clinician in an outpatient specialty clinic at his local VA Medical Hospital, where he worked on projects to improve patient and employee engagement and experience throughout the organization, as well as developing clinical educational guidelines and programs for the rehabilitation service line. In that role, Rafi led a team to roll out a patient-engagement initiative rooted in relationship-based care.

After leaving the VA, Rafi began working as a healthcare consultant, on a multimillion-dollar project for Georgia's Department of Behavioral Health and Developmental Disabilities. This project involved work related to the transition of individuals out of state institutions to community residences and establishing statewide mobile integrated clinical services for individuals on the state Medicaid waiver programs. As a part of that project, Rafi developed and launched a large internal marketing and communications campaign aimed at increasing awareness for internal stakeholders about integrated clinical services within the state. He also developed protocols and systems to coordinate and manage interdisciplinary collaborative care within the State's Medicaid Waiver system as well as clinical and operational guidelines for case management and telehealth, and virtual service delivery. His work on telehealth has been discussed in Forbes.

Rafi also has experience as an assistant professor at Augusta University's Occupational Therapy Program, as a Licensed Board Member on the GA State OT Board, has served on several committees for the national OT Board (NBCOT), and as a consultant to various private healthcare clinics and organizations. He also serves on the Board of Directors for NBCOT.

He is also the CEO and President of ProActive Rehabilitation and Wellness, a multidisciplinary outpatient specialty rehab clinic serving patients with chronic musculoskeletal and orthopedic conditions as well as those experiencing chronic pain.

At Rehab U Practice Solutions, Rafi helps clinics, health systems, and healthcare companies improve patient engagement and experience leading to increased revenue and lifetime patient value. He envisions a world where skilled, competent, and caring clinicians serve and care for engaged patients to promote better clinical outcomes, unmatched patient satisfaction, and lasting relationships.

Connect with Rafi:

LinkedIn: www.linkedin.com/in/rafaelsalazarii/

Rehab U Practice Solutions: https://rehabupracticesolutions.com

ProActive Rehabilitation and Wellness: https://pro-activehealth.com